Gareth Williams

Top Biology Grades for You

GCSE Revision Guide for AQA Modular

Contents

Revision Calendar (inserted, for your bedroom wall)

Revision Cards (detachable, for revision in spare moments)

To see the latest Exam Specification for AQA Modular Science, visit **www.aqa.org.uk**

To see this Exam Specification 'mapped' with the relevant pages in *Biology for You*, visit **www.biologyforyou.co.uk**

Introduction

Top Biology Grades for You is designed to help you achieve the best possible grades in your GCSE examination.

It focuses on exactly what you need to do to succeed in the AQA Modular Science exam (for Single or for Double Award, and at either Foundation or Higher Tier), or in the AQA Modular Biology exam.

There is a separate book for AQA Coordinated Science and AQA Biology B.

This revision book is best used together with the ***Biology for You*** textbook, but it can also be used by itself.

There are also books for
Top Physics Grades for You and
Top Chemistry Grades for You.

For each section in the AQA Modular Science examination specification, there is a Topic as shown on the opposite page.

For each Topic there are 2 double-page spreads:

- a **Revision** spread, which shows you exactly what you need to know (see below), and

- a **Questions** spread, which lets you try out some exam questions on this topic.
  The **Answers** for these, with Examiners' Tips, are given at the back of the book.

In addition, for each section of Topics there is:
- a **Sample Answer** spread, showing you answers at Grade-A level and at Grade-C level, with Examiners' Comments and Tips. These will help you to focus on how to improve, to move up to a higher grade.

Each Revision spread is laid out clearly, using boxes:

Each spread starts with some 'ThinkAbout' questions, to help you focus on the topic. The answers are shown at the bottom of the page.

Topic number 8.

The pages show essential content for the exam.

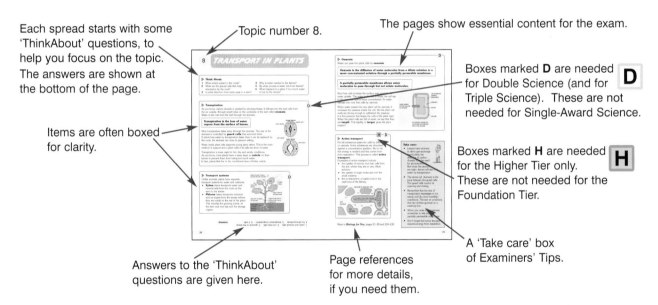

Items are often boxed for clarity.

Boxes marked **D** are needed for Double Science (and for Triple Science). These are not needed for Single-Award Science.

Boxes marked **H** are needed for the Higher Tier only. These are not needed for the Foundation Tier.

Answers to the 'ThinkAbout' questions are given here.

Page references for more details, if you need them.

A 'Take care' box of Examiners' Tips.

As a first step, go through this book and:
- If you are studying for Single-Award Science, cross out all the boxes labelled **D**

- If you are studying for the Foundation Tier, cross out all the boxes labelled **H**

- If you are **not** studying for Triple Award Biology, cross out all of Topics 21, 22, 23.

Then use the pull-out **Revision Calendar** to keep a record of your progress.

At the back of the book there are detachable **Revision Cards**, with very brief summaries. You can use these to top up your revision in spare moments – for example, when sitting on a bus or waiting for a lesson.

Best wishes for a great result in your exams.

Gareth Williams

Revision Technique

Prepare

1. Go through the book, crossing out any boxes that you don't need (as described at the bottom of page 3).

2. While doing this, you can decide which are your strong topics, and which topics that you need to spend more time on.

3. You need to balance your time between:
   - **Revising** what you need to know about Biology.
     To do this, use the first double-page spread in each topic.
   - **Practising** by doing exam questions.
     To do this, use the second spread in each topic.

   Do these two things for each topic in turn.

Revise

4. Think about your best ways of revising. Some of the best ways are to do something *active*. To use active learning you can:
   - Write down **notes**, as a summary of the topic (while reading through the double-page spread).
     Use highlighter pens to colour key words.
   - Make a **poster** to summarise each topic (and pin it up on your bedroom wall?).
     Make it colourful, and use images/sketches if you can.
   - Make a spider-diagram or **mind map** of each topic.
     See the example here, but use your own style:
   - Ask someone (family or friend) to **test** you on the topic.
   - **Teach** the topic to someone (family or friend).

   Which method works best for you?

5. It is usually best to work in a quiet room, for about 25–30 minutes at a time, and then take a 5–10 minute break.

6. After you have revised a topic, make a note of the date on the pull-out **Revision Calendar**.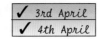

Practise

7. When you have revised a topic, and think you know it well, then it's important to practise it, by answering some exam questions. Turn to the second spread of the topic and answer the questions as well as you can.

8. When you have finished them, turn to the **Examination answers and tips** that start on page 108.
   Check your answers, and read the Examiners' Hints.
   Can you see how to improve your answers in future?

9. Keep a record of your progress on the **Revision Calendar**.

Re-revise and Top-up

10. It is important to re-revise each topic again, after an interval. The best intervals are after 10 minutes, after 1 day, and after 1 week (see the graphs in *Biology for You*, pages 388–389).

    For this top-up you can use the topic spread, your notes, poster or mindmap, and the **Revision Cards** at the back of this book.

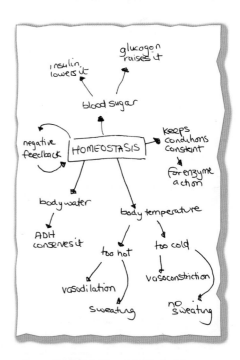

*Part of a **Mind Map** for Topic 11: Homeostasis.*

*A Mind Map always makes more sense when you make it **yourself**.*

A revision flowchart:

Choose a topic to revise.

1. Revise

- **Think About**: try the questions in the Think About box.
  The answers are at the bottom of the page.

- **Read** the rest of the double-page spread.
  Focus on any parts you are not sure about.

- **Do** make Notes, or a Poster, or a Mind Map.
  Highlight key points in colour.

- **Re-read** the spread after a break of 5–10 minutes.

- **Take care**: read the 'Take care' box.
  Can you see how you can use this advice?

- ✓ **Tick and date** the pull-out Revision Calendar.

2. Practise

- **Try** the questions on the double-page of questions.
  These are in the same style as the ones in the exam.

- **Check** your answers. The answers begin on page 108.
  Read the Examiners' Hints carefully.
  Go back over anything you find difficult.

- ✓ **Tick and date** the pull-out Revision Calendar to
  keep a record of your progress.

Then later:

Re-visit
Re-visit each topic 1 day later, and then 1 week later.
Read the double-page spread, your notes or Mind Map,
and the questions you answered.

Up your Grade
At the end of each section of topics, read the Sample
Answers at Grade A and Grade C in Getting the Grades.
Look at the Hints and Tips for improving your grade.

Top-up
Use the Revision Cards to remind you of the key points,
and test yourself.
Even better, make your own Revision Cards.

Examination Technique

Before the exam

1. Make sure you know the dates and times of all your exams, so that you are not late!
    See the table at the bottom of this page.

2. Make sure you know which topics are going to be examined on which paper.

3. On the night before the exam, it may help to do some quick revision – but don't do too much.
    Make sure you get a good night's sleep.

On the day of the exam

1. Aim to arrive early at the exam room.

2. Make sure that you are properly equipped with pens and pencils (including spares), a rubber, a ruler, a calculator (check the battery!) and a watch.

During the exam

1. Don't waste time when you get the paper. Write your name and candidate number (unless they are already printed). Read the instructions on the front page of the booklet, carefully, and make sure you follow them.

2. Read each question very carefully.
    In each question there is always a 'command' word that tells you what to do.
    If the question says '*State ...*' or '*List ...*' or '*Name ...*' then you should give a short answer.
    If the question says '*Explain ...*' or '*Describe ...*' or '*Why does ...*' or '*Suggest ...*' then you should make sure you give a longer answer.

    Put a ring round each 'command' word.

    Then <u>underline</u> the key words in the question.
    For example:

    Ⓒalculate the amount of <u>heat energy</u> which <u>tertiary</u> consumers transfer to the environment as a <u>percentage</u> of the energy received from <u>secondary</u> consumers. Ⓢhow your working.

    Then you can see exactly what is given to you in the question, and what you have to do.

    Make sure that you answer only the question shown on the exam paper (not the one that you wish had been asked).

One way of collecting information about all you exams (in all your subjects):

Date, time and room	Subject, paper number and tier	Length (hours)	Types of question: – structured? – single word answers? – longer answers? – essays?	Sections?	Details of choice (if any)	Approximate time per mark (minutes)
5th June 9.30 Hall	Science (Double Award) Paper 1 (Biology) Higher Tier	1½	Structured questions (with single-word answers and longer answers)	1	no choice	1 min.

Answering the questions

Structured questions

- Make sure you know exactly what the question is asking.

- Look for the number of marks awarded for each part of the question. For example *(2 marks)* means that the Examiner will expect 2 main (and different) points in your answer.

- The number of lines of space is also a guide to how much you are expected to write.

- Make sure that you use any data provided in the question.

- Pace yourself with a watch so that you don't run out of time. You should aim to use 1 minute for each mark. So if a question has 3 marks it should take you about 3 minutes.

- In calculations, show all the steps in your working. This way you may get marks for the way you tackle the problem, even if your final answer is wrong. Make sure that you put the correct units on the answer.

- Try to write something for each part of every question.

- Follow the instructions given in the question. If it asks for one answer, give only one answer.

- If you have spare time at the end, use it wisely.

Extended questions

- Some questions require longer answers, where you will need to write two or more full sentences.

- The questions may include the words '***Describe***...' or '***Explain***...' or '***Evaluate***...' or '***Suggest***...' or '***Why does***...'.

- Make sure that the sentences are in good English and are linked to each other.

- Make sure you use scientific words in your answer.

- As before, the marks and the number of lines will give you a guide of how much to write. Make sure you include enough detail with at least as many points as there are marks.

- For the highest grades you need to include full details, in scientific language, written in good English, and with the sentences linking together in the correct sequence.

For multiple-choice questions:
- Read the instructions carefully.
- Mark the answer sheet exactly as you are instructed.
- If you have to rub out an answer, make sure that you rub it out well, so no pencil mark is left.
- Even if the answer looks obvious, look at all the alternatives before making a decision.
- If you are not sure of the answer, then first delete any answers that look wrong.
- If you still don't know the answer, then make an educated guess!
- Ensure that you give an answer to every question.

1

▶ **Think About:**

1 What are 'the building blocks of life'?

2 What controls the cell and contains instructions to make more cells?

3 What controls materials passing into and out of cells?

4 Where do chemical reactions take place inside cells?

5 What is a tissue?

6 What is an organ?

▶ **Cell structure of animal cells**

All animal cells are composed of the following:

- a **nucleus** that controls everything that happens inside the cell and contains the information to make new cells;

- **cytoplasm**, a jelly-like substance in which the chemical reactions of the cell take place. These chemical reactions are controlled by **enzymes**;

- a **cell membrane** which gives the cell its shape and controls which substances enter and leave the cell.

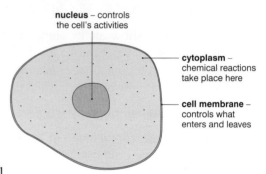

nucleus – controls the cell's activities

cytoplasm – chemical reactions take place here

cell membrane – controls what enters and leaves

▶ **Cell structure of plant cells**

A typical plant cell looks different from an animal cell. For one thing, it has a regular shape.

- A **cell wall** is found outside the cell membrane. This is made of **cellulose** and strengthens the cell.

- **Chloroplasts** are found in the cytoplasm of many plant cells. They absorb light energy to make food by photosynthesis.

- A **vacuole** is a large sac in the centre of the cytoplasm. It contains a watery fluid called **cell sap**.

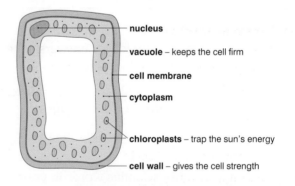

nucleus

vacuole – keeps the cell firm

cell membrane

cytoplasm

chloroplasts – trap the sun's energy

cell wall – gives the cell strength

▶ **Differences between plant and animal cells**

Plant cells	Animal cells
have tough cell walls for support	no cell walls
many have chloroplasts	no chloroplasts
have a large permanent vacuole, containing cell sap	some have small vacuoles, but no cell sap
many have a box-like shape	the shape varies

▶ **The mitochondrion**

Mitochondrion are small sausage-shaped structures that can only be seen clearly under an electron microscope. They are found in the cytoplasm of cells and release energy from respiration for the cell to use.

H

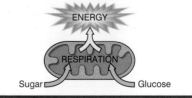

ENERGY

RESPIRATION

Sugar   Glucose

Answers: 1. cells   2. nucleus   3. cell membrane   4. in the cytoplasm   5. A group of identical cells which all do the same job.   6. An organ is made up of different tissues working together to do a particular job.

▶ Different cells

Many cells look different. This is because they have their own special job to do. Look at the **specialised** animal and plant cells. Try and remember how each has developed to do a particular job.

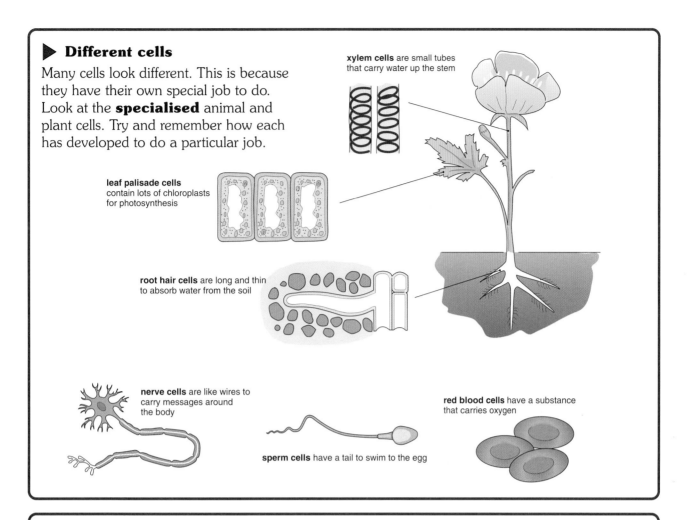

xylem cells are small tubes that carry water up the stem

leaf palisade cells contain lots of chloroplasts for photosynthesis

root hair cells are long and thin to absorb water from the soil

nerve cells are like wires to carry messages around the body

sperm cells have a tail to swim to the egg

red blood cells have a substance that carries oxygen

▶ Tissues and organs

- **Tissues** are groups of identical cells that all do the same job. For example, heart muscle cells form heart muscle tissue that beats throughout your life.
- **Organs** are made up of groups of tissues. For example, your heart is made up of muscle tissue, blood tissue and nerve tissue. These tissues all do different jobs, but work together to pump blood around your body. These work together to do a particular job.
- A number of organs working together makes up a **system**. Your heart and blood vessels make up your circulatory system. This transports blood to all the cells of your body.

Put all of the body's systems together and you get an **organism**.   That's you!

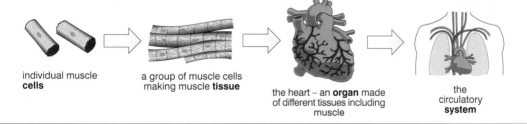

individual muscle **cells**

a group of muscle cells making muscle **tissue**

the heart – an **organ** made of different tissues including muscle

the circulatory **system**

More in **Biology for You**, pages 8–17.

Take care:
- Make sure that you know the similarities, and in particular the differences, between plant and animal cells.
- Learn at least *three* examples of specialised plant and animal cells and how they are adapted to do their job e.g. a sperm cell, a red blood cell, a leaf palisade cell, a root hair cell.

Examination Questions – Cells

Year 10 questions

1 The diagram shows a nerve cell. This cell passes information to other cells.

Match words from the list with each of the labels **1–4** on the diagram.

cell membrane

controls the activities of the cell

cytoplasm

passes information to other cells

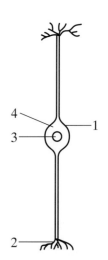

2 The diagram shows a cell from the leaf of a green plant.

Match words from the list with each of the labels **1–4** on the diagram.

contains cell sap

controls the activities of the cell

absorbs light energy to make food

strengthens the cell

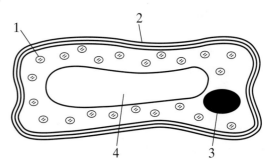

3 The diagrams show a white blood cell and a bacterial cell. (They are not drawn to the same scale.)

Match words from the list with each of the labels **1–4** on the diagrams.

cell membrane

cell wall

cytoplasm

nucleus

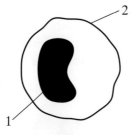

White blood cell

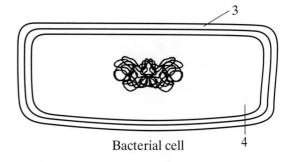

Bacterial cell

4 Human cells contain mitochondria.
Which **two** of the following are true of mitochondria?

they are found in the cytoplasm

they contain haemoglobin

they control the activity of the cell

they control the passage of chemicals in and out of the cell

they release energy during respiration

Year 11 questions

1 The diagram shows a sperm cell.

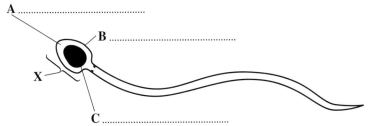

a) Use words from the list to label parts **A**, **B** and **C**.   Marks

   cell membrane   chloroplast   cytoplasm   nucleus   vacuole   (*3 marks*)

b) The part of the cell labelled **X** is 0.005 mm long.
   Approximately how long is the whole sperm cell?
   Circle the correct answer.

   0.00045 mm   0.0045 mm   0.045 mm   0.45 mm   (*1 mark*)

c) Which part of the sperm cell, **A**, **B** or **C**, controls the activity of the cell?

   .... (*1 mark*)

d) The sperm is a male gamete. It swims towards the female gamete.
   Use the information from the diagram to suggest **one** way in which the structure of the
   sperm helps it to swim.

   ....

   .... (*1 mark*) $\overline{6}$

2 Animal and plant cells have some features that are the same.
   There are some differences. Plant cells have a number of extra features.

a) Name three features shown by both animal and plant cells.
   Describe what function they each carry out.

   i Name... (*1 mark*)

      Function ....

      .... (*1 mark*)

   ii Name... (*1 mark*)

      Function ....

      .... (*1 mark*)

   iii Name... (*1 mark*)

      Function ....

      .... (*1 mark*)

b) State **three** ways in which plant cells differ from animal cells.

   i .... (*1 mark*)

   ii .... (*1 mark*)

   iii .... (*1 mark*) $\overline{9}$

2 Digestion

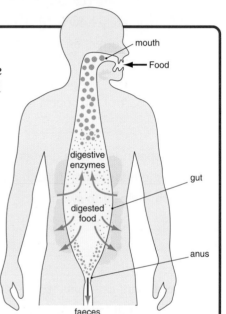

> ▶ **Think About:**
>
> 1 What is meant by 'a balanced diet'?
> 2 What do you need carbohydrates for?
> 3 What do you need proteins for?
> 4 What do you need fats for?
> 5 Can you name four other things needed for a balanced diet?
> 6 Why does our food need to be digested?
>
> 7 How does the food that we digest get to all parts of our body?
> 8 Put these parts of the digestive system into the correct order in which they affect food as it passes down the gut: stomach, large intestine, mouth, liver, small intestine, pancreas, gullet (oesophagus).

▶ Why digest?

Before your body can use the food that you have eaten it must be broken down into very small molecules. These can be **absorbed** into the bloodstream in the wall of the small intestine.

> **Digestion is the breakdown of large, insoluble food molecules into small soluble food molecules so that they can be absorbed into the bloodstream.**

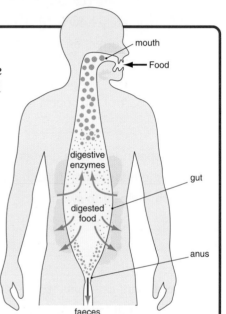

Digestion is speeded up by the action of **enzymes** (catalysts).

- Insoluble **starch** molecules are broken down into soluble **sugars**.
- This is catalysed by the enzyme **amylase**.
- Amylase is produced in the salivary glands, the pancreas and the small intestine.

Insoluble **protein** molecules are eventually broken down into soluble **amino acids**.

Protease enzymes catalyse this breakdown. They are produced by the stomach, the pancreas and the small intestine.

Insoluble **lipids** (fats and oils) are broken down into **fatty acids** and **glycerol**. **Lipase** enzymes catalyse this breakdown. Lipases are produced by the pancreas and the small intestine.

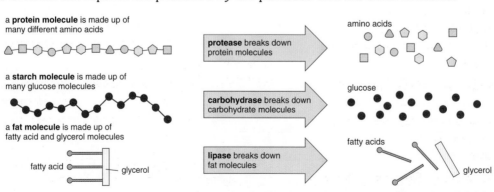

a **protein molecule** is made up of many different amino acids

protease breaks down protein molecules

amino acids

a **starch molecule** is made up of many glucose molecules

carbohydrase breaks down carbohydrate molecules

glucose

a **fat molecule** is made up of fatty acid and glycerol molecules

fatty acid — glycerol

lipase breaks down fat molecules

fatty acids

glycerol

Answers:
1. a diet with the right variety of foods and the right amounts of foods.   2. energy   3. for growth and the repair of cells   4. as a store of energy and for insulation.   5. vitamins, mineral salts, fibre and water   6. so that it can be absorbed into our bloodstream.   7. It is carried around the body in our bloodstream.   8. mouth, gullet (oesophagus), stomach, small intestine, liver, pancreas, large intestine

► In the stomach

Your stomach is a muscular bag that will hold up to two litres of food.

- The stomach makes digestive juices that contain protease.
- The proteases start the digestion of the proteins to amino acids.
- The stomach produces hydrochloric acid.
- The protease enzymes work best in acid conditions.
- The acid also kills most of the bacteria taken in with the food.

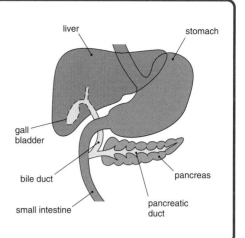

► In the small intestine

The **liver** produces **bile**, a sticky, green alkaline fluid.

Bile is stored in the **gall bladder** before passing down the **bile duct** into the small intestine. In the small intestine bile neutralises the acid food coming through from the stomach. Bile provides the alkaline conditions in which the enzymes in the small intestine work best. These enzymes that complete digestion are produced by the **pancreas** and the small intestine.

Bile also **emulsifies** fats. This means that it breaks large drops of fat down into small droplets. This increases the surface area of the fat for lipase enzymes to act upon.

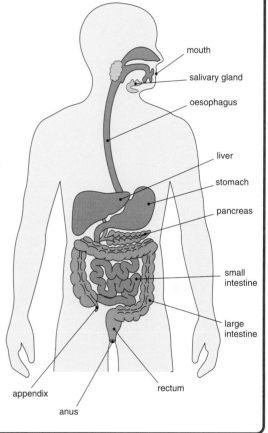

► What next?

In the small intestine the soluble food is absorbed into the bloodstream.

The soluble sugars, amino acids, fatty acids and glycerol pass through the wall of the small intestine and are carried around the body in the bloodstream (*see* page 29).

In the **large intestine** much of the water is reabsorbed into the blood. What remains is mainly indigestible food (fibre), dead cells, bacteria and some water.

This solid waste or **faeces** is stored in the **rectum** before leaving the body through the **anus**.

More in *Biology for You*, pages 57–61.

Take care:

- Each part of the digestive system has a particular function (job). Make sure that you learn the parts and where the enzymes are produced.

- You may be asked to label parts of the digestive system on a diagram in the exam.

- You need to know the names of the enzymes that digest carbohydrates, proteins and fats. A clue comes from the chemical that they digest: so carbohydrases digest carbohydrates, proteases digest protein and lipases digest lipids (fats).

Examination Questions – Digestion

Year 10 questions

1 The diagram shows the human digestive system.

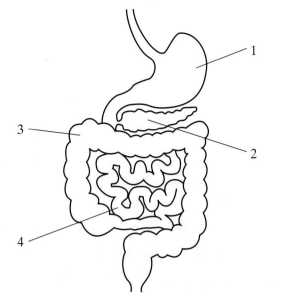

Choose the best labels to add to the diagram.

pancreas   **large intestine**

small intestine   **stomach**

2 Which **two** of the following are enzymes?

amino acids   **glucose**   **lipase**   **protease**   **starch**

Questions 3 to 6

The information is from a box containing breakfast cereal.

	Amount per 100 g
Energy	1800 kg
Protein	6 g
Carbohydrate	83 g
Fat	3 g

3 The recommended daily intake of energy for a young adult male is 12 000 kJ.
A 40 g serving of cereal will provide….

   A $\frac{3}{100}$ (3%) of the daily requirement for energy.

   B $\frac{6}{100}$ (6%) of the daily requirement for energy.

   C $\frac{15}{100}$ (15%) of the daily requirement for energy.

   D $\frac{3}{10}$ (30%) of the daily requirement for energy.

4 The amount of protein that a young adult female needs each day is 60 g.
How much cereal would the female have to eat to get this amount of protein?

   A 10 g   **B** 100 g   **C** 500 g   **D** 1000 g

5 During digestion the starch in the cereal will be broken down into….

   A amino acids   **B** fatty acids   **C** glycerol   **D** sugars

6 Starch digesting enzymes are produced in the …..

   A pancreas and small intestine.

   B salivary glands only.

   C salivary glands, pancreas and small intestine.

   D small intestine only.

Year 11 questions

1 The diagram shows what happens to the food that you eat.

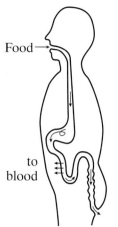

Food →

to blood

Part of body	Time spent there by food
mouth	a few seconds
gullet	a few seconds
stomach	2–4 hours
intestines	10–20 hours

Marks

a) Choose words from this list to complete the sentences below.

anus   blood   small intestine   stomach

The food you eat is broken down into soluble substances.

These substances are then absorbed through the walls of your ....

so that they can pass into your ....

Undigested food (faeces) passes out of your body through your ....

(3 marks)

b) i In which part of your digestive system does food spend the longest time?
Underline the correct answer.

mouth   gullet   stomach   intestines   *(1 mark)*

ii How long does it take for food to pass all the way through your digestive system?

....

(2 marks)

6

2 Bread contains starch, protein and fat.

a) Complete each sentence by choosing the correct words from the box.

amino acids   protein   fat   starch   fatty acids   sugar

Amylase speeds up the digestion of .... The product of this

digestion is .... Protease speeds up the digestion of

.... The products of this digestion are ....

(4 marks)

b) Why do molecules of starch, protein and fat need to be digested?

....

....

(2 marks)

6

3 Breathing and respiration

> **Think About:**

1. Where does breathing take place in your body?
2. What structures protect your lungs?
3. Your windpipe splits into two branches, one enters each lung. What are they called?
4. What is the diaphragm?
5. What are the alveoli?
6. Where does respiration take place?
7. What gas is used during respiration?
8. What gas is produced during respiration?
9. What is the fuel that is used up during respiration?

D

> **Your breathing system**

Your breathing system takes air into and out of your body so that **oxygen** can diffuse out of the air into the bloodstream and **carbon dioxide** can diffuse out of the bloodstream into the air.

The movement of air into and out of the lungs is called **ventilation**.

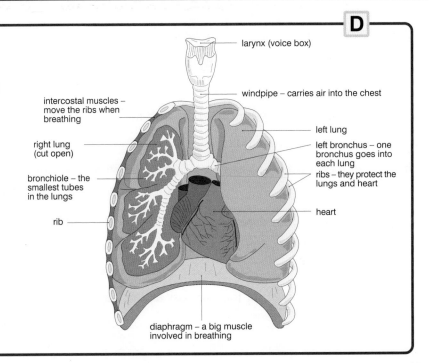

larynx (voice box)

windpipe – carries air into the chest

intercostal muscles – move the ribs when breathing

right lung (cut open)

left lung

left bronchus – one bronchus goes into each lung

bronchiole – the smallest tubes in the lungs

ribs – they protect the lungs and heart

rib

heart

diaphragm – a big muscle involved in breathing

D

> **Breathing movements**

- To inhale (breathe in) the muscles between your ribs contract to raise the ribs upwards and outwards.

H
- The muscles in your **diaphragm** contract causing your diaphragm to flatten.
- These two movements cause the volume inside your thorax to increase.
- The pressure inside your thorax decreases resulting in atmospheric air entering your lungs. When you breathe out your breathing muscles act in the opposite way.
- Deep inside your lungs the air reaches your **alveoli**. These are tiny air sacs which have a very large surface area, are moist and have a rich supply of blood capillaries, so gases can easily diffuse into and out of your blood (see page 29).

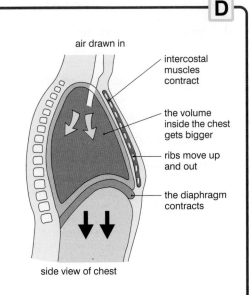

air drawn in

intercostal muscles contract

the volume inside the chest gets bigger

ribs move up and out

the diaphragm contracts

side view of chest

▶ Aerobic respiration

Aerobic respiration involves using oxygen to break down glucose and release energy.

glucose + oxygen ⟶ carbon dioxide + water + energy

Your body uses this energy to build large molecules from the small ones, to enable muscles to contract and to maintain a steady body temperature.

Respiration occurs inside our cells in structures called mitochondria. Energy from respiration is also used in **active transport**.

▶ Respiration without oxygen

During vigorous exercise your heart and lungs can not get enough oxygen to your muscles quickly enough. The muscles become **fatigued** and stop contracting efficiently. This results in a shortage of oxygen and means that the muscles may carry out **anaerobic respiration** for a time. Anaerobic respiration is respiration in the absence of oxygen. The glucose becomes broken down to **lactic acid**.

glucose ⟶ lactic acid + energy

The body needs to break down this waste product, lactic acid. Extra oxygen is needed to break the lactic acid down to carbon dioxide and water. The extra oxygen needed is called the **oxygen debt**.

Take care:
- Breathing and respiration are **not** the same thing. Breathing results in gas exchange at the alveoli. Respiration results in the release of energy inside cells.
- Remember that when volume inside the thorax **increases**, the pressure inside **decreases**.
- This causes air to be forced into the lungs by atmospheric pressure. Air is *not* sucked in.

More in **Biology for You**, pages 69–87.

Answers: 1. in the lungs   2. the ribs   3. bronchi (singular: bronchus)   4. a sheet of muscle just below your rib cage   5. tiny air sacs deep inside your lungs where gas exchange takes place between the air and your blood   6. in all the cells of the body   7. oxygen   8. carbon dioxide   9. glucose (sugar)

Examination Questions – Breathing and respiration
Year 10 questions

Questions **1**, **2** and **3** are based on the following diagram.

The diagram shows part of the thorax.

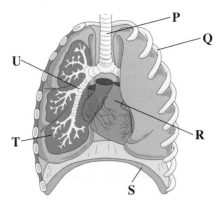

1 Which parts make air move into the lungs?

    A P and Q   **B** P and U   **C** Q and R   **D** Q and S

2 The movement of air into and out of lungs is called…

    A circulation   **B** diffusion   **C** respiration   **D** ventilation

3 In which part does oxygen move into the blood?

    A P   **B** R   **C** S   **D** T

Respiration is the process during which energy is released.
This energy comes from the food we have digested.

4 The food substance which is used in respiration is…

    A glucose   **B** glycerol   **C** lipase   **D** starch

5 The gas released during aerobic respiration is ……

    A carbon dioxide   **B** lactic acid   **C** nitrogen   **D** oxygen

6 During vigorous exercise, our muscles obtain energy from both aerobic and anaerobic respiration.

  Match words from the list with each of the spaces 1–4 in the sentences.

    glucose   **lactic acid**   **oxygen**   **water**

  Anaerobic respiration in a muscle may happen when there is a shortage of …… **1**……. .

  Anaerobic respiration is the incomplete breakdown of …… **2**……. .

  Oxygen debt is the amount of oxygen needed to oxidise …… **3**…… into carbon dioxide

  and …….**4**……. .

7 Which of the following occurs when muscles surrounding the thorax contract to bring about inhalation?

    A   The volume of the thorax increases and the pressure inside it decreases

    B   The volume of the thorax decreases and the pressure inside it increases

    C   The volume of the thorax and the pressure inside it both decrease

    D   The volume of the thorax and the pressure inside it both increase

Year 11 questions

1 The diagram shows the breathing system.

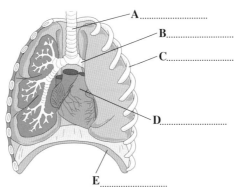

A............................

B............................

C............................

D............................

E............................

    a) i In which part of the body are the breathing organs found?

....

(1 mark)

       ii On the diagram, name the structures labelled **A** to **E**.   *(5 marks)*

    b) Describe, in as much detail as you can, the job of the breathing system.

....

....

....

(3 marks)

9

2 A student exercised for
5 minutes then rested for
55 minutes. The graph shows
how the lactic acid content of
the student's blood changed
during this 60 minute
period.

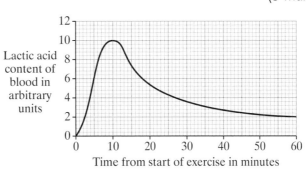

    a) Describe the effects of exercise and rest on the lactic acid content of the student's blood.

....

....

....

(3 marks)

    b) i Why does the body produce lactic acid during exercise?

....

....

(1 mark)

       ii During exercise an oxygen debt builds up.
          Explain what is meant by *oxygen debt*.

....

....

(2 marks)

6

BLOOD and CIRCULATION

▶ Think About:

1 What pumps the blood around your body?

2 Where is this structure found?

3 What are the tubes called that carry blood around your body?

4 What does the blood take away from the lungs?

5 What does the blood take back to the lungs?

6 What does the blood take away from the small intestine?

7 What are the two main types of blood vessel called?

8 What tissue is most of the heart made up of?

▶ Your heart

Your heart is made up of two muscular pumps side by side. The right side of the heart pumps blood to the lungs. The left side of the heart pumps blood all round the body.

Blood enters the **right atrium** from the rest of the body. It is **deoxygenated** since it has little oxygen left in it. The atrium contracts and forces blood into the **right ventricle**. The ventricle contracts to force blood out of the heart to the lungs. **Valves** prevent the blood from flowing backwards.

Blood returning from the lungs is **oxygenated** (full of oxygen). It enters the **left atrium**, which then contracts forcing the blood into the **left ventricle**.

The ventricle contracts to force blood out of the heart to the body. Again valves ensure that blood flows in the correct direction.

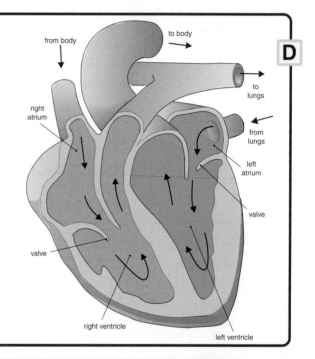

D

▶ Blood vessels

Blood flows *away* from the heart in **arteries**.
Arteries have thick walls containing muscle and elastic tissue.

Blood flows *back* to the heart in **veins**. Veins have thinner walls and often have **valves** to prevent the back-flow of blood.

In the organs of the body blood flows through very narrow vessels called **capillaries**, which are only one cell thick. Substances needed by the cells in body tissues pass out of the blood through thin capillary walls. Substances produced by the cells pass through the walls in the opposite direction.

There are two separate circulation systems, one to the lungs and one to all the other organs of the body. This is called a **double circulation**.

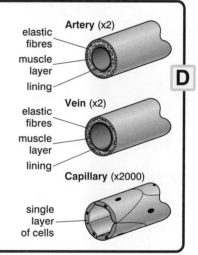

D

▶ Parts of the blood

> **Blood is made up of red cells, white cells and bits of cells called platelets. All of these are carried in a liquid called plasma.**

Plasma is a yellow liquid in which the blood cells are suspended. Plasma transports:
- carbon dioxide made in respiration from the organs to the lungs;
- the soluble products of digestion (such as sugars and amino acids) from the small intestine to other organs;
- **urea** from the liver to the kidneys.

White blood cells are large cells that have a distinct nucleus. They help defend the body against microbes as part of the immune system.

Platelets are not cells at all. They are small fragments of cells and have no nucleus. Platelets help the blood to clot at the site of a wound.

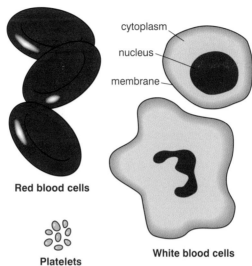

Red blood cells

Platelets

White blood cells

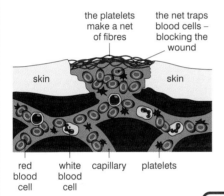

the platelets make a net of fibres

the net traps blood cells – blocking the wound

skin   skin

red blood cell   white blood cell   capillary   platelets

Red blood cells transport oxygen from the lungs to the organs where it is used in respiration. They are flattened discs with a large surface area for the absorption of oxygen.

H

Red cells have no nucleus, but are packed with a red pigment called **haemoglobin**.

Haemoglobin combines with oxygen in the lungs to form **oxyhaemoglobin**. This is carried by the red cells to other organs in the body. Here the oxyhaemoglobin splits up into haemoglobin and the oxygen is released to the cells for respiration.

More in **Biology for You**, pages 88–105.

in the lungs

haemoglobin + oxygen   **oxyhaemoglobin**

in the tissues

Take care:
- In exams, heart diagrams are drawn as you would view a heart placed in front of you. So the chambers on the **left-hand** side of the diagram are the right atrium and the right ventricle.
- Remember that the walls of the capillaries are so thin that substances can easily diffuse in and out through their walls.
- Usually veins carry deoxygenated blood, *except* for the pulmonary vein coming back from the lungs.
- Usually arteries carry oxygenated blood, *except* for the pulmonary artery carrying blood to the lungs.

Examination Questions – Blood and circulation

Year 10 questions

1 The list contains the names of **four** parts of the blood.

Match up the parts of the blood to the job they do.

plasma   platelets   red blood cell   white blood cell

carries oxygen	1
carries glucose and carbon dioxide	2
help to form a scab over a wound	3
eat bacteria and produce antibodies	4

Use the data in the following table to answer questions 2 and 3.

The volume of blood pumped by the heart changes during vigorous exercise.

The table shows the effect of exercise on the heart of a fit athlete.

	At rest	Moderate exercise	Strenuous exercise
Volume of blood pumped out of the heart in cm^3 per minute	6592	16 688	
Volume of blood pumped out of the heart during each heartbeat in cm^3	103	149	155
Heart rate in beats per minute	64	112	159

2 The volume of blood pumped out of the heart during strenuous exercise is ….

A 9300 cm^3 per minute

B 9540 cm^3 per minute

C 24 645 cm^3 per minute

D 558 000 cm^3 per minute

3 The percentage increase in the volume of blood pumped out of the heart during each heart beat when the heart rate changes from 64 to 159 beats per minute is….

A 33.45%

B 40.25%

C 50.49%

D 66.45%

4 Which of the following reactions occurs in red blood cells passing through the muscle capillaries?

A haemoglobin + oxygen → oxyhaemoglobin

B haemoglobin + carbon dioxide → oxyhaemoglobin

C oxyhaemoglobin → haemoglobin + oxygen

D oxyhaemoglobin → haemoglobin + carbon dioxide

Year 11 questions

1 The diagram shows a section through the heart and the blood vessels connected to it.

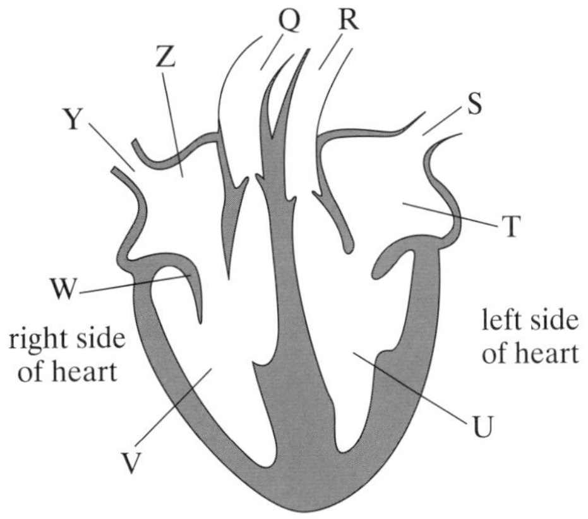

a) Which part Q to Z:

  i is the left ventricle; ....

  ii prevents blood flowing from the right ventricle to the right atrium; ....

  iii is a vein carrying blood with a high concentration of carbon dioxide; ....

  iv is an artery carrying blood rich in oxygen? ....

  (4 marks)

b) Describe in as much detail as you can, how oxygen is transported by the blood and then enters the tissues.

....

....

....

....

....

  (3 marks)

  7

2 The diagrams show sections through an artery and a vein.

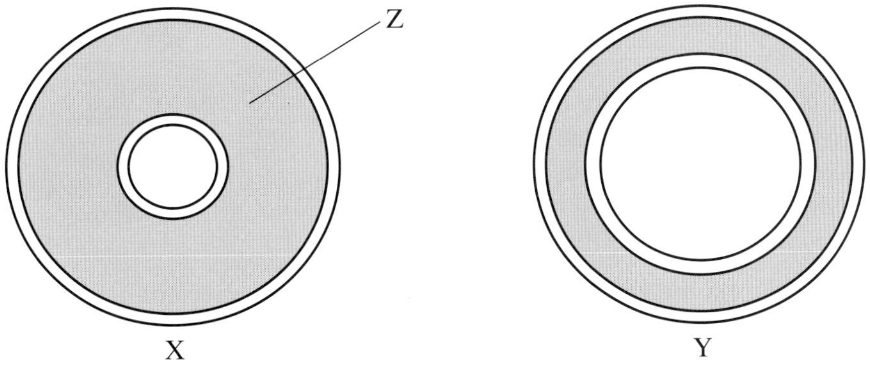

X

Y

a) Which of these diagrams X or Y, shows a vein. Give the reason for your answer.

....

....

  (1 mark)

b) Name two types of tissue found at Z.

  1 ....

  2 ....

  (2 marks)

c) Veins and the heart contain valves.
  What is the job of valves in the circulatory system?

....

....

  (1 mark)

  4

5

▶ Think About:

1. Many diseases are caused by microscopic living things, what are they called?
2. What are the three main types of microbes called?
3. What happens to bacteria and viruses if they get into your body?
4. What do bacteria and viruses produce that make you feel ill?
5. Viruses reproduce inside our cells. How does this end up damaging them?
6. What is a vaccine?
7. How can a vaccination make you immune to a disease?
8. Give two examples of diseases *not* caused by microbes.

▶ Types of microbes

Bacteria are different from animal cells.
Yes, they do have a cell membrane and cytoplasm, but there are three main differences:
- Bacterial cells do not have a proper nucleus.
- They *do* have a cell wall outside the cell membrane.
- They are much smaller.

Viruses are not really cells at all.
- They have a protein coat outside them.
- Inside they have just a few genes.

Genes carry the information that controls the activities of the cell. Viruses can only live and reproduce *inside* other cells. They invade a healthy cell, using its genetic material to make more virus particles, the cell bursts and the viruses escape to invade more healthy cells.

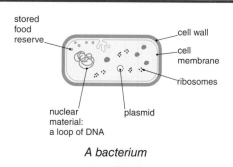

A bacterium

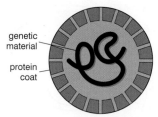

A virus

This damage to the living cells and the **toxins** (poisons) that viruses and bacteria make, produce the **symptoms** of disease, such as high temperature and headache.

▶ How are germs spread?

Diseases are more likely to spread if large numbers of microbes enter the body as a result of unhygienic conditions or contact with infected people.

Microbes can enter our body in the air we breathe. When an infected person sneezes or coughs tiny drops of liquid shower the air.

You can pick up germs by touching an infected person or things that an infected person has used, such as towels, combs or cups.

Food and drink can be infected with germs. Typhoid and Cholera are spread in infected water. Salmonella can be found in infected food that has not been thoroughly cooked to kill the bacteria.

How many ways of spreading disease can you find here ?

▶ Barriers to disease

The body has a number of ways of stopping microbes from getting in.
- The skin acts as a barrier to germs.
- The air passages to the lungs make a sticky liquid called **mucus** that traps the germs. Tiny hairs called **cilia** push it up to the throat where it is swallowed.
- If you get a cut the blood forms a **clot** to seal the cut.

▶ Immunity

White blood cells defend the body against invading microbes by:
- ingesting (eating) the microbes and destroying them with enzymes;
- producing **antibodies** which destroy particular bacteria and viruses;
- making **antitoxins**, which neutralise the toxins (poisons) released by the microbes.

Once a person has made the antibodies against a particular bacterium or virus, the white blood cells can quickly produce them again if re-infection occurs so that a person has become **immune** to that particular disease microbe.

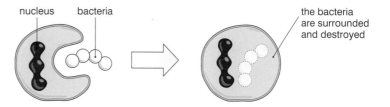

▶ Vaccination

You don't have to catch a disease to become immune to it. You can gain immunity from a **vaccine**.

A vaccine contains a mild or dead form of the bacterium or virus. When the vaccine is introduced to the body it stimulates the white cells to produce antibodies.

Once you have been **vaccinated**, your immune system will be able to react very rapidly and produce antibodies if you are infected by the same germs again.

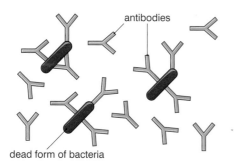

The dead bacteria stimulate white cells to make antibodies

More in ***Biology for You***, pages 171–184.

Take care:
- Do not confuse antibodies with antitoxins. Antibodies kill disease microbes, antitoxins neutralise the toxins they produce.

- When the body is immune to disease, it is not because the antibodies are in the blood for a long time. Immunity means that the white cells are 'primed' to produce lots of antibodies if re-infection occurs.

- Remember that antibodies are *specific* to a certain disease microbe, so that any antibody that gives you immunity to chicken pox won't give you immunity to mumps.

Examination Questions – Disease

Year 10 questions

1 Bacteria and viruses both cause diseases.

Which **two** of the following are true of bacteria and viruses?

    A they are both micro-organisms

    B they both contain cytoplasm

    C they both contain genes

    D they both have a nucleus

    E they both have a protein coat

2 White blood cells defend the body against bacteria.

Which **two** of the following are produced by white blood cells to defend the body against bacteria?

    A antibodies

    B antitoxins

    C mucus

    D toxins

    E vaccine

3 When people are vaccinated, they are injected with …

    A dead or weakened microbes.

    B drugs to destroy the microbes.

    C microbes to destroy the toxins.

    D white blood cells.

4 The list contains the names of **three** microbes that cause disease.

Match up the microbes with the way they are most often spread.

    flu virus   **salmonella**   **typhoid**

    1 infected food

    2 infected water

    3 through the air

Year 11 questions

1 a) The diagrams show a virus and a bacterium (not drawn to the same scale).

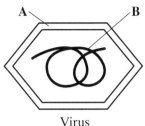
Virus

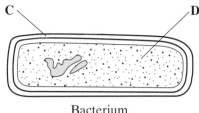
Bacterium

Use words from the list to identify parts **A** to **D**.

cell wall	**chloroplast**	**cytoplasm**
genes	**nucleus**	**protein coat**

A ....

B ....

C ....

D ....

(4 marks)

b) Give **two** ways in which the body stops microbes getting into it.

1 ....

....

2 ....

....

(2 marks)

6

2 We may catch a disease if large numbers of microbes enter the body.

a) Name **two** types of microbe that can cause disease in the body.

1 ....

2 ....

(3 marks)

b) How does mucus in the lungs protect us from disease?

....

....

(1 mark)

c) Which organ in the body produces acid to kill microbes?

....

(1 mark)

d) Which type of blood cell destroys microbes?

....

(1 mark)

6

6 DIFFUSION

▶ **Think About:**

1 What gas passes into your cells?
2 What gas passes out of your cells?
3 Where does oxygen pass out of the air into your blood?
4 Where do digested food products pass into your blood?
5 Where are waste chemicals, like urea, filtered out of the blood?
6 Where exactly do water and mineral salts pass into root?

▶ Diffusion in animals

D

When they pass into our bodies, dissolved substances need to cross the surfaces of organs. To get in and out of our cells, dissolved substances have to cross the cell membranes.

> **Diffusion is the movement of particles from a region of high concentration to a region of lower concentration until they are spread out evenly.**

These particles may be in the form of a gas or they may be any substance in solution.
The greater the difference in concentration, the faster the rate of diffusion.

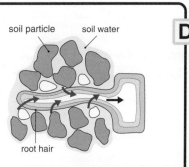

▶ Into and out of cells

D

Your body cells need food and oxygen to release energy. This food and oxygen are carried in the bloodstream to every cell in your body. When they reach the cells, the food and oxygen **diffuse** into the cells through the **cell membrane**.

As the cells use up food and oxygen, they make waste materials, like carbon dioxide. These would poison the cells if they were to build up. So carbon dioxide and other waste chemicals diffuse out of the cells into the bloodstream through the cell membrane.

▶ Diffusion in plants

D

Water and mineral salts are taken up from the soil in the roots. The roots have **root hair cells** that have a large surface area. This makes it easier for water and mineral salts to diffuse out of the soil into the root hair cells.

Leaves have a flattened shape and many internal air spaces. This increases the surface area over which diffusion of gases like carbon dioxide, oxygen and water vapour can occur.

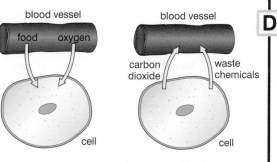

Water passes into a root hair cell

▶ Gas exchange in the lungs

As you know, in the lungs, oxygen diffuses from the air in the **alveoli**, into the bloodstream. Carbon dioxide diffuses out of the bloodstream into the air inside the alveoli. These gases diffuse across the cell membranes of the cells of the alveoli.

The alveoli are well adapted for diffusion to take place because:

- they provide a very large surface area for diffusion;
- they are moist, so the gases can dissolve;
- they have thin walls (only one cell thick) so the gases do not have to diffuse very far;
- they have a good blood supply so that oxygen is quickly removed and carbon dioxide quickly supplied. This maintains a **diffusion gradient**.

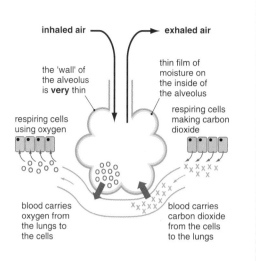

▶ Absorption in the small intestine

Digested food, like sugars and amino acids, are **absorbed** into the blood in the small intestine. The small intestine is specialised for absorption. It has:

- a thin lining,
- a good blood supply,
- a very large surface area.

This large surface area is due to the small intestine being very long (at least 6 metres), having a folded inner lining and having millions of tiny, finger-like projections called **villi** (singular of villi is **villus**).

From the diagram, you can see that each villus is well adapted for **absorption**. It has:

- a large surface area (it is long and thin),
- a thin lining (one cell thick),
- a good capillary blood supply.

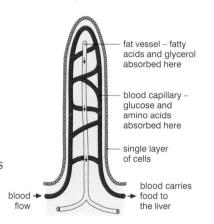

Take care:

- Not all substances pass into and out of cells by diffusion. Some move by **active transport**, using energy released in respiration. (See page 39.)

- Be *specific* about which substances are diffusing e.g. if it is oxygen, then say oxygen. Don't just say '*it*' moves from a high concentration to a low concentration.

- Don't just say a particular structure 'has a large surface area', explain how. For example, in the case of a root hair cell it has a large surface area because it is so long.

More in *Biology for You*, pages 18–20, 61, 77, 226.

Answers: 1. oxygen 2. carbon dioxide 3. the alveoli 4. the small intestine 5. the kidneys 6. root hair cells

Examination Questions – Diffusion
Year 10 questions

1 Oxygen passes through the wall of an alveolus into the blood by

    A active transport

    B diffusion

    C dissolving

    D osmosis

2 Which one of the following is the main process by which oxygen enters a root hair cell?

    A active transport

    B diffusion

    C dissolving

    D osmosis

3 Which one of the following is the main process by which nitrate ions enter a root hair cell?

    A active transport

    B diffusion

    C dissolving

    D osmosis

4 Which one of the following is the main process by which water enters a root hair cell?

    A active transport

    B diffusion

    C dissolving

    D osmosis

5 The list contains four features of the alveoli.

  Match up the features **A** to **D** with the adaptations for diffusion **1** to **4**.

    A They provide a large surface area.

    B They are moist.

    C They have thin walls.

    D They have a good blood supply.

    1 gases can dissolve

    2 small diffusion distance

    3 maintains a diffusion gradient

    4 large amount of membrane in contact with gases

6 Use words from the list to complete the sentences.

    capillaries   folded   increased   long   smooth   villi

  The small intestine is very ....**1**....... .

  Its inner surface is ....**2**....... .

  The inner surface area is ....**3**....... by finger-like projections called ......**4**...... .

  Each of these has ......**5**...... .

Year 11 questions

1 Describe in as much detail as you can, how gases enter and leave the blood in the lungs.

....

....

....

....

....

(4 marks)   4

2 Explain in as much detail as you can:

   a) what the term 'diffusion' means;

....

....

....

....

(3 marks)

   b) what determines the net direction in which diffusion takes place;

....

....

....

....

(2 marks)

   c) what factors determine the rate of diffusion?

....

....

....

....

(2 marks)   7

Getting the Grades – Humans as organisms

Try this question, then compare your answer with the two examples opposite ▶

1   a) i Complete the following word equation for aerobic respiration.

Glucose + oxygen → .... + water + energy   [1]

ii Where does this take place inside a cell?

.... [1]

iii Animals use some of the energy released when its cells respire to move.
Give **two other** uses.

1 ....

2 .... [2]

b) During prolonged vigorous exercise a time is reached when insufficient oxygen reaches
the muscles.

i Name the type of respiration that takes place if these muscles carry on contracting?

.... [1]

ii This type of respiration differs from the process summarised in the word equation in a) i.
The waste produced and the amount of energy released from a molecule of glucose
is different.
How do they differ?

waste produced

....

....

....

amount of energy released

....

....

.... [3]

iii Describe in as much detail as you can, what an oxygen debt is.

....

....

....

....

....

....

.... [3]

This candidate used information well and shows a good understanding of this area of the specification.

1 a) i carbon dioxide ✓
      ii It takes place in an organelle called ✗
      iii 1 To build up complex molecules from
             simpler ones. ✓
           2 Maintain a steady body temperature in
             the cold. ✓
   b) i Anaerobic respiration ✓
       ii Carbon dioxide and water are produced in
           aerobic respiration whereas lactic acid is
           produced in anaerobic respiration. ✓
           Anaerobic respiration produces less energy. ✓
       iii Anaerobic respiration produces lactic acid
            as a waste product. ✓ Cells need oxygen to
            oxidise the lactic acid to carbon dioxide
            and water. ✓
            The amount of oxygen needed is the
            oxygen debt. ✓

9 marks = Grade A answer

▶ **Improve your Grades   A up to A***

To get an A* you must complete all parts of the question. This candidate couldn't remember 'mitochondria' at the first attempt. Perhaps the answer was not revisited before the completion of the paper. Go back over your work and make some attempt at an answer. Do not leave parts unanswered.

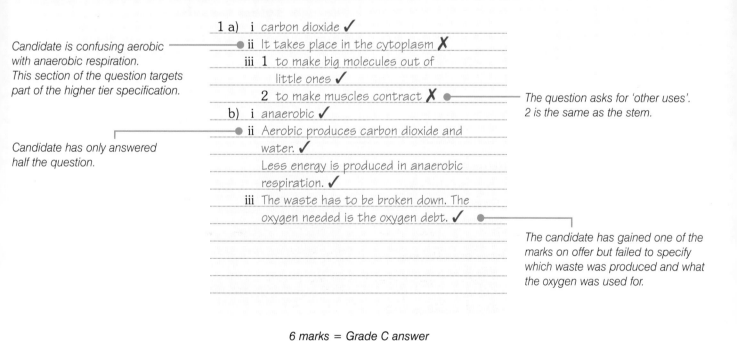

Candidate is confusing aerobic with anaerobic respiration. This section of the question targets part of the higher tier specification.

1 a) i carbon dioxide ✓
      ii It takes place in the cytoplasm ✗
      iii 1 to make big molecules out of
             little ones ✓
           2 to make muscles contract ✗

The question asks for 'other uses'. 2 is the same as the stem.

   b) i anaerobic ✓
       ii Aerobic produces carbon dioxide and
           water. ✓

Candidate has only answered half the question.

           Less energy is produced in anaerobic
           respiration. ✓
       iii The waste has to be broken down. The
            oxygen needed is the oxygen debt. ✓

The candidate has gained one of the marks on offer but failed to specify which waste was produced and what the oxygen was used for.

6 marks = Grade C answer

▶ **Improve your Grades   C up to B**

If you are asked to give the difference between two things describe them both to show what the difference is, or use comparative language.

7 photosynthesis

> ## Think About:
>
> 1 What chemical does green plants use to trap sunlight?
> 2 Which gas is needed for photosynthesis to take place?
> 3 Which gas is given off by a plant during photosynthesis?
> 4 What structures within leaf cells contain chlorophyll?
> 5 How does carbon dioxide get into the cells of a leaf?
> 6 After photosynthesis, what is glucose stored as in a leaf?
> 7 How do plants use some of the oxygen given off during photosynthesis?
> 8 In what tissue in a leaf are most chloroplasts found?

D

▷ Photosynthesis

Photosynthesis is the process by which plants make their own food. To do this they need a source of energy to build food molecules. Sunlight is absorbed by the green substance called **chlorophyll**. Chlorophyll is found inside the **chloroplasts** of some plant cells.

Light energy is used to convert carbon dioxide and water into glucose.

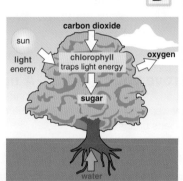

$$\textbf{carbon dioxide} + \textbf{water} \xrightarrow{\text{light and chlorophyll}} \textbf{glucose} + \textbf{oxygen}$$

Carbon dioxide enters the leaf of a plant by diffusion through the stomata. Water is absorbed from the soil by the roots and carried up the stem to the leaves in the **xylem vessels**.

Plants use some of the glucose in respiration to get their own energy. Excess glucose can be stored in the leaf as insoluble starch. When we test a leaf for starch with iodine, it will turn blue–black.

Oxygen is released as a by-product of photosynthesis.

▷ The rate of photosynthesis

If you look back at the equation you can see what is needed for photosynthesis.
The *rate* of photosynthesis may be limited by:
- shortage of light – on a dull or cloudy day;
- shortage of carbon dioxide – on a sunny, warm day;
- low temperature – on a cold day.
- If any of these three factors are limiting then the rate of photosynthesis will decrease.

D

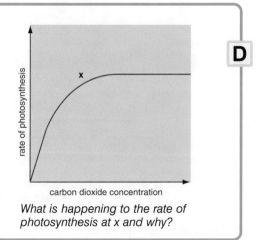

What is happening to the rate of photosynthesis at x and why?

Answers:
1. chlorophyll 2. carbon dioxide 3. oxygen 4. chloroplasts 5. through the stomata
6. starch 7. in respiration 8. palisade tissue

34

The products of photosynthesis

D
H

Green plants make make glucose (sugar) during photosynthesis. This glucose can be used by the plant in respiration to release energy. This energy can be used to build large molecules from small ones :

* sugars can be converted into insoluble **starch** and stored in the roots;
* sugars can be changed into **cellulose** which forms new cell walls;
* sugars can combine with nitrates and other nutrients to form **amino acids**. These can then be used to build **proteins** for plant growth;
* sugars can be converted into **lipids** (fats and oils) and stored in seeds.

H D

Healthy growth

Plants need more than just carbon dioxide and water for healthy growth. They also need **mineral ions** or **nutrients** which are found in the soil and absorbed by the plant's roots. These include:

* **Nitrate** is needed to make proteins. If it is lacking in the soil, the plant's growth will be stunted and older leaves will be yellow.
* **Phosphate** is needed for both photosynthesis and respiration. Lack of phosphate results in poor root growth and purple younger leaves.
* **Potassium** helps the enzymes involved in photosynthesis and respiration to work. Yellow leaves with dead spots shows that potassium is lacking in the soil.

Leaves

D

Leaves are well adapted to carry out photosynthesis.
They have:

* **a large surface area** – to absorb light rays;
* **a thin shape** – so gases can diffuse in and out easily;
* **chloroplasts** – which contain chlorophyll to absorb light energy;
* **veins** – to support the leaf and carry substances to and from all of the cells of the leaf.

Leaf structure

D

Look at this drawing of a thin slice of a leaf as seen under the microscope. You need to be able to name *all* the parts and describe their functions.

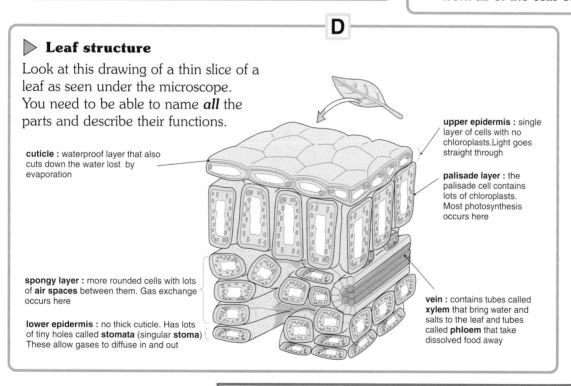

cuticle : waterproof layer that also cuts down the water lost by evaporation

spongy layer : more rounded cells with lots of **air spaces** between them. Gas exchange occurs here

lower epidermis : no thick cuticle. Has lots of tiny holes called **stomata** (singular **stoma**) These allow gases to diffuse in and out

upper epidermis : single layer of cells with no chloroplasts.Light goes straight through

palisade layer : the palisade cell contains lots of chloroplasts. Most photosynthesis occurs here

vein : contains tubes called **xylem** that bring water and salts to the leaf and tubes called **phloem** that take dissolved food away

More in **Biology for You**, pages 205–223.

Take care:

* Have you noticed that the equation for photosynthesis is the reverse of the equation for respiration?
* In photosynthesis, energy (in the form of light energy has to be put into the process). In respiration the energy is released to do work in the body.

Examination Questions – Photosynthesis
Year 10 questions

Questions **1–4** are based on the following drawing of a leaf.

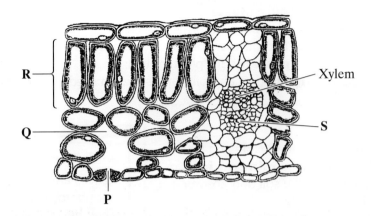

1 During photosynthesis, carbon dioxide moves from **P** to **Q** because…

    A it is warmer inside the leaf.

    B the chloroplasts are giving out oxygen.

    C there is a higher concentration of carbon dioxide at **P** than at **Q**.

    D water vapour is moving out from **Q** to **P**.

2 Most photosynthesis takes place in region **R** because these cells…

    A are close to the source of water.

    B are nearest to the supply of carbon dioxide.

    C are the largest.

    D contain most chlorophyll.

3 Sugar produced by photosynthesis can be stored in the leaf as…

    A glucagon.   **B** glucose.   **C** nitrates.   **D** starch.

4 The cells labelled **S** carry…

    A starch to the leaf.

    B sugar to the roots.

    C water to the growing regions.

    D water to the leaf cells.

5 The drawing shows a section through a leaf. Match words from the list with each of the labels **1–4** on the drawing.

    a waxy material

    carries sugar away from the leaf

    controls water loss from the leaf

    where most glucose is produced

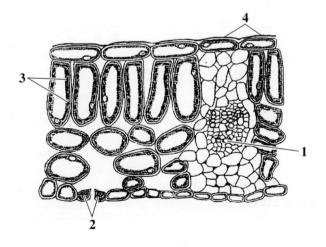

Year 11 questions

1 a) The equation describes the process of photosynthesis.   Marks

      Carbon dioxide + ... + light energy → glucose + ...

      i Write in the names of the **two** missing substances.   (2 marks)

      ii Name the green substance which absorbs the light energy.

      .... (1 mark)

   b) i In bright sunlight, the concentration of carbon dioxide in the air can limit the rate of
          photosynthesis. Explain what this means.

      ....

      ....

      .... (2 marks)

      ii Give **one** environmental factor, other than light intensity and carbon dioxide
          concentration, which can limit the rate of photosynthesis.

      .... (1 mark)   6

2 The graph shows the rates at
   which a potato plant and a
   maize plant produce sugar
   (glucose) at different
   temperatures.

   a) Describe how the rate of
       glucose production of
       the potato plant changes
       as the temperature
       increases from 0°C to 40°C.

   ....

   ....

   ....

   ....

   .... (4 marks)

   b) i What do we call the process that plants use to make sugar (glucose)?

       .... (1 mark)

      ii What is the other product of this process?

       .... (1 mark)

   c) Describe **three** ways in which the rate of glucose production of the maize plant is
       different from the rate of glucose production of the potato plant.

       1 ....

       2 ....

       3 .... (3 marks)   9

8 TRANSPORT IN PLANTS

▶ Think About:

1 What enters a plant in the roots?
2 What are the special cells that help absorption by the roots?
3 In what direction does water pass in a stem?
4 Why is water needed in the leaves?
5 By what process is water lost from leaves?
6 What happens to a plant if too much water is lost by the leaves?

▶ Transpiration

D

As you know, carbon dioxide is needed for photosynthesis. It diffuses into the leaf cells from the air outside, through small holes on the underside of the leaf called **stomata**.
Water is also lost from the leaf through the stomata.

> **Transpiration is the loss of water vapour from the surface of leaves.**

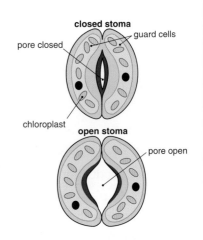

Most transpiration takes place through the stomata. The size of the stomata is controlled by **guard cells** that surround them.
If plants lose water by transpiration faster than it can be replaced by the roots, the stomata can close to prevent wilting.

Water inside plant cells supports young plant stems. This is the main method of support and a plant wilts if its cells are short of water.

Transpiration is more rapid in hot, dry and windy conditions.
As you know, most plants have a waxy layer or **cuticle** on their leaves to prevent them from losing too much water.
In fact, plants that live in dry conditions have a thicker cuticle.

▶ Transport systems

D

Unlike animals, plants have separate transport systems for water and nutrients.

- **Xylem** tissue transports water and mineral salts from the roots up the stem to the leaves.
- **Phloem** tissue transports nutrients such as sugars from the leaves (where they are made) to the rest of the plant. This includes the growing points, at the stem and root tips and the storage organs.

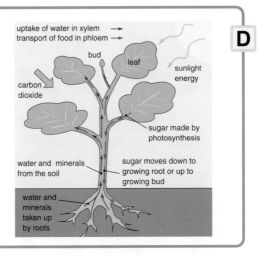

▷ Osmosis

Water can pass into plant cells by **osmosis**.

> **Osmosis is the diffusion of water molecules from a dilute solution to a more concentrated solution through a partially permeable membrane.**

> **A partially permeable membrane allows water molecules to pass through but not solute molecules.**

Root hair cells increase the surface area available for water uptake. The water in the soil is dilute, the cell sap in the root hair cells is more concentrated. So water diffuses into root hair cells by osmosis.

When water passes into any plant cell by osmosis, it increases the pressure inside the cell. But the plant cell walls are strong enough to withstand the pressure. It is this pressure that keeps the cells of the plant rigid. When the plant cells are full of water, we say that they are **turgid**. This rigidity or **turgor** gives the plant support.

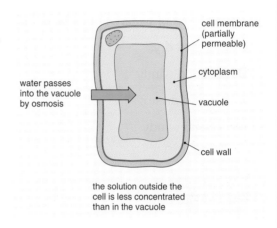

cell membrane (partially permeable)

cytoplasm

water passes into the vacuole by osmosis

vacuole

cell wall

the solution outside the cell is less concentrated than in the vacuole

---

H D

▷ Active transport

Not all substances pass into cells by diffusion or osmosis. Some substances are absorbed against a concentration gradient. But to do this energy is needed and this comes from from respiration. This process is called **active transport**.

Examples of active transport include:

- the uptake of ions by root hair cells from the soil, where they are in very dilute solution;
- the uptake of sugar molecules into the small intestine;
- the re-absorption of useful ions in the nephrons of the kidney.

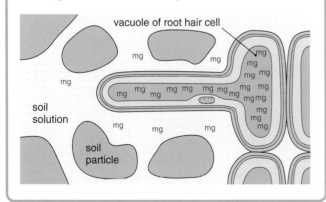

vacuole of root hair cell

mg

soil solution

soil particle

More in **Biology for You**, pages 21–28 and 224–232.

Take care:

- Leaves have stomata to allow gas exchange (particularly the diffusion of carbon dioxide in to be used for photosynthesis). But when the stomata are open, leaves will also lose water by transpiration.

- The stoma (pl. stomata) is the pore between the guard cells. The guard cells control its opening and closing.

- Remember that the rate of transpiration *increases* in hot, windy and dry (low humidity) conditions. The sort of conditions that dry clothes quickest on a washing line.

- When you write about osmosis remember to talk about a partially permeable membrane.

- Don't forget that active transport requires energy from respiration.

Examination Questions – Transport in plants
Year 10 questions

1 The loss of water vapour from plant leaves is called…

    A osmosis.

    B photosynthesis.

    C respiration.

    D transpiration.

2 The rate of loss of water vapour by a leaf is greatest when the weather is…

    A cool and dry.

    B cool and windy.

    C hot and damp.

    D hot and windy.

Questions 3 and 4 use data from the table below.

The table shows the mass of water that is absorbed by a plant and the mass of water vapour that is lost, at different times during the day.

Time of day	Rate of water absorption in g per hour	Rate of water vapour loss in g per hour
04.00	1.5	0.25
08.00	1.5	2.00
12.00	3.6	5.00
16.00	5.5	7.5
20.00	3.3	2.5
24.00	2.0	0.75

3 The net change in mass of the plant due to water uptake and loss at 12.00 is…

    A -1.4 g per hour.

    B 0.72 g per hour.

    C 8.6 g per hour.

    D 18 g per hour.

4 At which time is the plant most likely to show signs of wilting?

    A 08.00

    B 12.00

    C 16.00

    D 20.00

Year 11 questions

1 a) Root hair cells are found on the surface of young roots.

   Their cellulose cell walls are totally permeable to water and mineral ions.

   The cell membrane found at the surface of the cytoplasm of these cells and their vacuoles are partially permeable.

   Water in the soil forms a dilute solution. The cell sap found in root hair cells is a more concentrated solution.

   i The surface area of a root hair cell is large. Why is this important to the plant?

   ....

   ....

   ....

   (2 marks)

   ii What does the term **partially permeable** mean?

   ....

   (1 mark)

   iii Explain how water moves from the soil into the root hair cell vacuole.

   ....

   ....

   ....

   ....

   ....

   (3 marks)

   b) Some substances are moved by a process known as active transport.

   Cells involved in active transport often have larger numbers of mitochondria.

   i Describe **two** examples of active transport.

   1 ....

   ....

   ....

   2 ....

   ....

   ....

   (2 marks)

   ii Suggest a reason for the larger numbers of mitochondria present in cells involved in active transport.

   ....

   ....

   ....

   (2 marks)

Plant hormones

▷ Control of growth

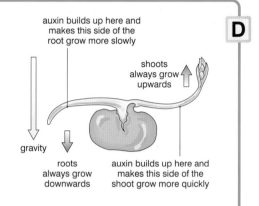

Which ever way a seed is planted, the root always grows *down* and the shoot always grows *upwards*.

Plant growth is controlled by a hormone called **auxin**. If a plant is put on its side, the auxin builds up on the lower side of the shoot or root.

In a shoot the auxin stimulates it to *grow more* on the lower side. This causes the shoot to bend upwards.

In a root the auxin also builds up on the lower side. But auxin *slows down* growth in a root, so the upper side grows quicker than the lower side and the root bends downwards. Roots also tend to grow towards water, down in the soil.

D

▷ Using plant hormones

D

Plant hormones are used commercially by humans to:

- produce large numbers of plants quickly by using rooting powder.
  This contains a hormone that stimulates the growth of roots from **cuttings**.
- regulate the **ripening** of fruits on the plant during transport to customers.
  Bananas are shipped in from thousands of miles away. The unripe fruit is kept in cold storage to delay ripening. It is then treated by hormones to ripen the fruit ready for sale.
- kill weeds by disrupting their normal growth patterns.
  Synthetic auxins kill the weed by making it grow too fast, this makes them thin and spindly and they soon die. The hormones are sprayed on broad-leaved weeds which are killed whilst the narrow-leaved grasses and cereal crops are unaffected.

Dipping a cutting in rooting powder.

More in **Biology for You**,
pages 243–245.

Answers:
1. down 2. up 3. towards the light
4. to get the light that they need for photosynthesis
5. light, gravity and moisture

DRUGS

> ## Think About:
> 1 Can you name three harmful drugs?
> 2 Can you name three helpful drugs?
> 3 What parts of the body can excess alcohol damage?
>
> 4 What addictive drug is present in tobacco?
> 5 Name a disease caused by smoking.

> ## What are drugs?
> Drugs and solvents are powerful chemicals that can change how you think, feel and behave. Remember that not all drugs are harmful. Some drugs such as aspirin can help people.
>
>
>
> *All these are examples of drugs*
>
> | A drug is a chemical that affects the way the nervous system works. |
> | --- |
>
> **Stimulants** are drugs that speed up the nervous system e.g. caffeine and cocaine. Depressants slow the nervous system down e.g. heroin and barbiturates.
>
> A person can become **dependent** upon certain drugs if they start to take them regularly. **Addiction** means that the person has become so dependent on the drug that it is doing them serious harm. If they stop taking the drug, they can suffer **withdrawal symptoms** without it.

> ## Alcohol
> Alcohol is a socially acceptable drug, but it can:
> - affect the nervous system by slowing down reactions and if too much is taken, it may lead to lack of self-control, unconsciousness or even a coma;
> - alcohol abuse can cause long-term damage to the liver and brain.
>
>
>
> ½ pint beer (0.3 litre)   1 glass sherry   1 single whisky   1 glass wine   ½ pint cider (0.3 litre)
>
> *All these drinks contain 1 unit of alcohol*

> ## Tobacco
> Tobacco smoke contains chemicals that can cause:
> - lung cancer;
> - other lung diseases such as bronchitis and emphysema;
> - diseases of the heart and blood vessels.
>
> Tobacco smoke also contains the gas, carbon monoxide, which reduces the ability of the blood to carry oxygen. In pregnant women this can prevent the fetus from getting enough oxygen and lead to a low birth mass.
>
>
>
> *Other people's smoke*
>
> | Carbon monoxide gas combines with haemoglobin in the red blood cells and prevents them from carrying oxygen. | **H** |
> | --- | --- |

More in *Biology for You*, pages 83–84 and 185–189.

Answers:
1. cocaine, heroin, ecstacy etc. 2. insulin, aspirin, penicillin etc.
3. the liver and brain, but also the stomach and heart 4. nicotine
5. bronchitis, emphysema, lung cancer, heart disease

Examination Questions – Plant hormones
Year 10 questions

1 Figure 1 shows two potted plants, **X** and **Y**, of the same age an size

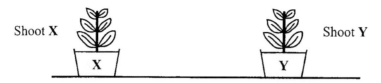

Shoot **X**   Shoot **Y**

Figure 1

Plant **X** was placed in the light, but plant Y was placed in a black box with a hole in one side.

Figure 2 shows the plants after 5 days

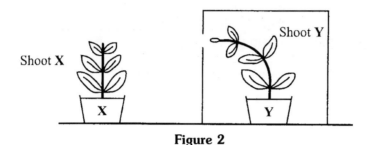

Shoot **X**   Shoot **Y**

Figure 2

Which **two** of the following are correct?

both shoots have grown towards moisture

both shoots have grown in the direction of the force of gravity

shoot **Y** has grown against the force of gravity but shoot **X** has not

shoot **Y** has grown more than shoot **X**

shoot **Y** has grown towards light from one side but shoot **X** has not

2 Plants respond to their surroundings.

Which **two** of the following are plant response?

roots grow away from moisture

roots grow in the direction of the force of gravity

shoots grow in the direction of the force of gravity

shoots grow towards light

shoots grow towards moisture

3 Use words from the list to complete the sentences.

auxin   gravity   light   inhibits   stimulates

High concentration of growth hormone ...... 1...... root growth.

...... 2...... inhibits shoot growth.

Plant roots and shoots are affected by a growth hormone called ...... 3...... .

Rooting powder can be used to ...... 4...... root growth in cuttings.

Shoots grow away from ...... 5...... .

Examination Questions – Drugs

Year 10 question

1 The table is about the effects of some substances on the body.

Match words from the list with each of the numbers **1–4** in the table.

alcohol

carbon monoxide

nicotine

tobacco

Substance	Effect on body
1	may cause lung cancer
2	may cause damage to liver and brain
3	is the addictive substance in cigarettes
4	reduces the amount of oxygen which the blood carries

Year 11 questions

1 Explain as fully as you can, why solvents should not be inhaled.

Marks

....

....

....

....

....

....

(3 marks)   3

2 Drugs like barbiturates and heroin are called depressants. They are known as
tranquillisers. Drugs like amphetamines and cocaine are known as stimulants.

a) Explain how depressants act on the nervous system.

....

....

b) How would amphetamines and cocaine affect the nervous system?

....

....

c) What is meant by the following terms:

  i tolerance   ii addiction   iii withdrawal symptoms.

(5 marks)   5

10 NERVOUS SYSTEM

Boo!

Think About:

1 Can you name the five senses?

2 What makes up your central nervous system?

3 How is information passed around your body?

4 What is a reflex?

5 Can you give an example of one reflex that protects your body?

Receptors

All of our actions start with a **stimulus** (a change that we can detect). **Receptors** are cells that can detect stimuli.

Look at the table to see which receptors respond to different stimuli.

Information from receptors passes along cells in nerves called **neurones** to the brain. The brain co-ordinates the **response**.

Stimulus	Receptor
light	eyes
sound and balance	ears
taste and smell	nose and tongue
touch, pressure and temperature change	skin

How the body reacts to a stimulus

Reflex actions often include *three* neurones: sensory, relay and motor. They interact as follows:

- Impulses from the receptor pass along the **sensory neurone** to the brain or spinal cord.
- At a junction (**synapse**) between the sensory neurone and a **relay neurone** in the brain or spinal cord, a chemical is released which triggers off an impulse in the relay neurone.
- A chemical is again released into the synapse between the relay neurone and a **motor neurone**.
- This causes an impulse to pass along the motor neurone to the effector, a muscle or gland.
- The effector brings about a response so the muscle contracts or the gland releases a chemical substance.

H

stimulus → receptor → coordinator → effector → response

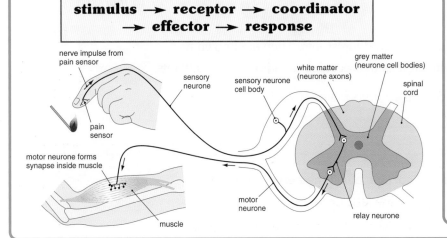

nerve impulse from pain sensor

pain sensor

sensory neurone

sensory neurone cell body

white matter (neurone axons)

grey matter (neurone cell bodies)

spinal cord

motor neurone forms synapse inside muscle

motor neurone

relay neurone

muscle

Reflexes

Many responses to stimuli are automatic and rapid. These are called **reflex actions**. In a simple reflex action, electrical impulses pass from the receptor along a **sensory neurone** to the brain or spinal cord. The impulse then passes along a **motor neurone** to a muscle or gland (the **effector**). The muscle or gland brings about a **response**. An example of a reflex action is coughing.

Answers:

1. sight, hearing (and balance), smell, taste, touch   2. brain and spinal cord   3. as electrical impulses along nerve cells   4. an automatic, rapid response to a stimulus   5. hand withdrawn from a hot object, blinking, coughing

▷ The eye

The eye is a good example of a receptor. Light from an object enters the eye through the **cornea**. The cornea and the **lens** bend the light rays to produce an image on the light-sensitive **retina**. Receptor cells in the retina send impulses to the brain along sensory neurones in the **optic nerve**.

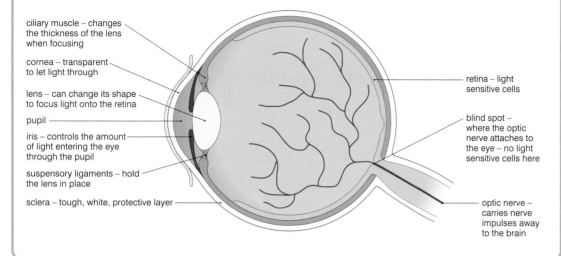

ciliary muscle – changes the thickness of the lens when focusing

cornea – transparent to let light through

lens – can change its shape to focus light onto the retina

pupil

iris – controls the amount of light entering the eye through the pupil

suspensory ligaments – hold the lens in place

sclera – tough, white, protective layer

retina – light sensitive cells

blind spot – where the optic nerve attaches to the eye – no light sensitive cells here

optic nerve – carries nerve impulses away to the brain

▷ Focusing

To focus on a **near** object, the ciliary muscles **contract**, the sensory ligaments **slacken** and the lens becomes **fatter**. This shape of lens focuses the near object on the retina.

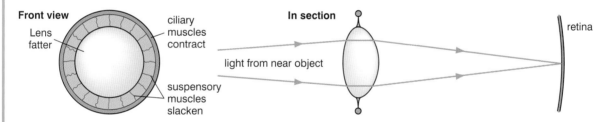

Front view
Lens fatter
ciliary muscles contract
suspensory muscles slacken

In section
light from near object
retina

To focus on a **distant** object, the ciliary muscles **relax**, the sensory ligaments **tighten** and the lens is pulled into a **thinner** shape. This shape of lens focuses the distant object onto the retina.

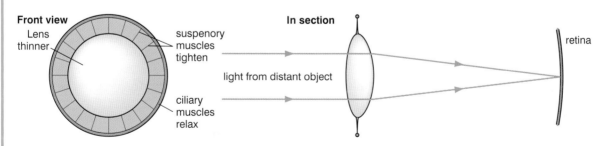

Front view
Lens thinner
suspenory muscles tighten
ciliary muscles relax

In section
light from distant object
retina

Take care:
- The cornea bends the light rays far more than the lens does.
- Always talk about the 'nerve impulses' *not* 'messages'.
- Nerves and neurones are not the same thing. A nerve is made up of hundreds of individual cells called neurones.

More in **Biology for You**, pages 118–136.

Examination Questions – Nervous system

Year 10 questions

1 Use words from the list to complete the sentences.

impulses   neurones   protect   reflex

Sense organs detect changes and send messages along our ....1........ .

These messages are called nerve ...... 2...... .

Automatic ....3....... actions happen very quickly to ...... 4...... your body.

The diagram below is for questions 2 to 5.

The diagram shows a reflex action.

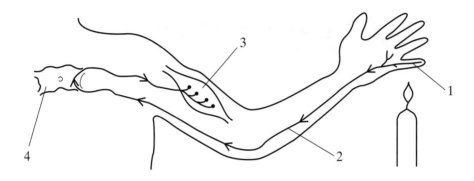

2 What is the stimulus shown in this diagram?

    A pressure   **B** light   **C** taste   **D** temperature

3 The receptor is the part labelled ...

    A 1   **B** 2   **C** 3   **D** 4

4 The effector is labelled ...

    A 1   **B** 2   **C** 3   **D** 4

5 The response will be ...

    A close eyes   **B** move hand   **C** run away   **D** sweating

Reflex actions are involved in some of the body's responses.

6 Which of the following describes the path taken by an impulse in a reflex action?

    A effector → sensory neurone → relay neurone → motor neurone

    B receptor → sensory neurone → relay neurone → motor neurone

    C sensory neurone → motor neurone → relay neurone → synapse

    D synapse → receptor → relay neurone → sensory neurone

7 The function of a synapse is to ...

    A detect changes in temperature.

    B produce nerve impulses in a receptor.

    C stimulate a gland.

    D transfer an impulse from one neurone to another.

Year 11 questions

1 Lasers can be used to remove tissue from the front of the eye. This operation corrects short-sightedness.

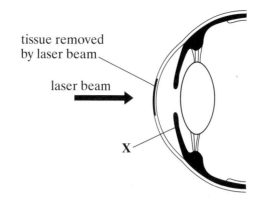

tissue removed by laser beam

laser beam

X

Marks

a) i Name the part of the eye from which tissue is removed by the laser.

.... *(1 mark)*

ii Give one job of this part of the eye.

....

.... *(1 mark)*

b) i Name the part of the eye labelled **X** on the diagram.

.... *(1 mark)*

ii What is the job of this part of the eye?

....

....

How does it do this job?

....

....

(5 marks)   8

2   a) Name **two** stimuli that receptors in the skin can detect.

.... and .... *(2 marks)*

b) i What is the job of a synapse?

....

.... *(2 marks)*

ii How does it work?

....

....

(3 marks)

c) Draw a flow diagram to summarise the stages in a spinal reflex.

(3 marks)   10

11 Homeostasis

▷ Think About:

1 What are the chemicals called that control chemical reactions inside your body?
2 What particular conditions do enzymes need to work best?
3 What happens to the level of sugar in your blood after a high carbohydrate meal?
4 What does being 'warm blooded' mean?
5 What does being 'cold blooded' mean?
6 How does your body respond on a very hot day?

▷ Homeostasis means

keeping conditions inside the body constant. Conditions such as temperature, water level, sugar level, pH of the blood and carbon dioxide level.

These constant conditions allow our enzymes to work efficiently.
Many of these conditions are controlled by **hormones**. Hormones are produced by glands and are transported to their target organs in the bloodstream.

D

▷ Diabetes

Our blood glucose level is controlled by two hormones: **insulin** and **glucagon**. Both of these hormones are released by the **pancreas**.

Diabetics are unable to control their blood sugar level properly. They can not make enough insulin and so the concentration of glucose in their blood may become dangerously high. This can make them tired and thirsty. Sometimes the blood sugar

level can fall too low. The person can feel weak, irritable and confused; they may even faint.

Diabetes can be successfully treated by following a low-glucose diet or by injecting with exactly the right dose of insulin. Diabetics often carry glucose tablets or a drink around with them.

D **H**

▷ Controlling blood sugar

It is the pancreas that monitors and controls blood glucose level.

After a high carbohydrate meal blood glucose will be too high. The pancreas detects this and releases insulin into the blood. Insulin causes the **liver** to convert glucose to insoluble **glycogen**. The liver removes the glycogen from the blood and stores it and so your blood sugar level returns to normal.

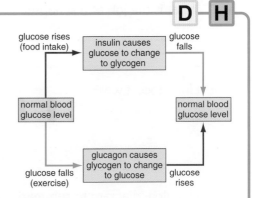

After a lot of exercise or fasting, your blood sugar will be too low. The pancreas detects this and releases a different hormone, glucagon, into the blood. Glucagon causes the liver to convert glycogen into glucose and release it into your blood. So your blood sugar returns to normal.

Answers: 1. enzymes 2. the best temperature, pH and water content 3. it rises 4. Your body temperature stays more or less constant even if the outside temperature changes. 5. The body temperature can not be controlled and kept constant. It will change as the outside temperature changes. 6. you sweat and your skin looks flushed

▷ Controlling body temperature

Your body temperature is controlled by receptors in your brain. These form the **thermoregulatory centre**. This part of the brain monitors the temperature of the blood running through it. This is your **core body temperature**. Also temperature receptors in the skin send impulses to this centre, giving it information about skin temperature.

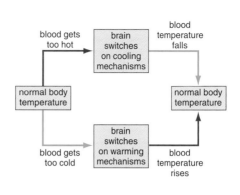

When it's hot

- Blood vessels supplying the capillaries at your skin surface **dilate** (widen) so that more blood reaches the surface of your skin and more heat is lost by radiation. So you look flushed.

- Sweat glands in your skin release more sweat, which cools the body as it evaporates.

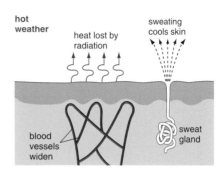

Getting colder

- Blood vessels supplying the capillaries at your skin surface **constrict** (get narrower) so that less blood reaches the surface of your skin and less heat is lost by radiation. So you look pale.

- Sweat glands stop making sweat.

- Your muscles may start to contract rapidly and you 'shiver'. These contractions need respiration which produces extra heat energy and these warm your body.

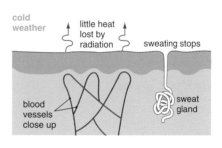

Take care:

- Remember that it is the pancreas and *not* the brain that monitors your blood sugar level.

- The liver is responsible for converting glucose to glycogen and storing it. Similarly, the liver converts glycogen to glucose and releases it into the blood when it is needed.

- It is the small branches of arteries, the **arterioles**, which dilate and constrict *not* the capillaries.

- Sweating releases sweat onto the skin surface. It is the evaporation of this sweat that cools the skin.

- Do not get mixed up by the words glucagon and glycogen.
  Glucagon is a hormone that converts glycogen to glucose.
  Glycogen is a carbohydrate food store in the liver.

More in *Biology for You*, pages 106–110.

Examination Questions – Homeostasis

Year 10 questions

1 Use organs from this list to complete the table.

bladder   kidneys   lungs   pancreas

control the amount of carbon dioxide in blood	1
controls the amount of water in the blood	2
releases a hormone to control the amount of sugar in blood	3
stores urine	4

2 Which one of the following is normal body temperature?

    A 13°C   **B** 30°C   **C** 37°C   **D** 73°C

3 What is the name given to the process of keeping things constant inside us?

    A circulation   **B** excretion   **C** homeostasis   **D** responding

4 Which one of the following helps to cool you down?

    A digestion   **B** shivering   **C** sweating   **D** transpiring

5 Which one of the following helps to keep you warm?

    A digestion   **B** shivering   **C** sweating   **D** transpiring

6 Body temperature is controlled by the brain.

Which **two** of the following contain receptors involved in temperature control?

pancreas   pituitary gland   skin   sweat glands   thermoregulatory centre

The graph shows the effect of a 10 minute exercise period on the core body temperature of an athlete.

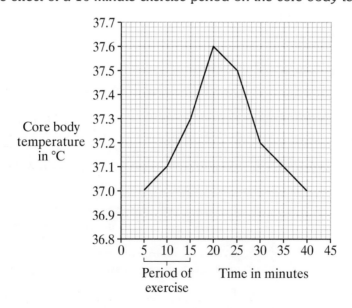

7 By how much did the core body temperature continue to rise after the end of the exercise period?

    A 0.3°C   **B** 0.6°C   **C** 5.0°C   **D** 37.6°C

8 What was the average rate of fall in body temperature between 20 and 35 minutes?

    A 0.008°C per minute   **B** 0.033°C per minute   **C** 0.1°C per minute   **D** 0.5°C per minute

Year 11 questions

1 The graph shows the concentration of glucose in the blood of two people.

Person **A** is a non-diabetic.

Peson **B** has diabetes.

Each person ate 75 grams of glucose at 1.0 hours.

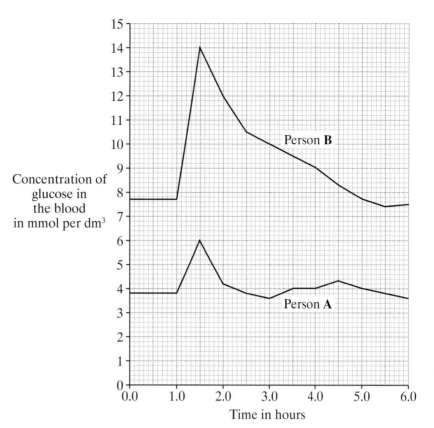

Concentration of glucose in the blood in mmol per dm³

Time in hours

Marks

a) i What was the maximum concentration of glucose in the blood of Person **A**?

.... mmol per dm³

(1 mark)

ii After eating the glucose, how long did it take for the concentration of glucose in the blood of Person **B** to return to normal?

.... hours

(1 mark)

b) A diabetic person does not produce enough insulin.

i Which organ produces insulin?

....

(1 mark)

ii Write the letter **X** on the graph to show one time when the blood of Person **A** would contain large amounts of insulin. *(1 mark)*

c) A high concentration of glucose in the blood can harm body cells as a result of osmosis. Explain why.

....

....

....

....

....

....

(4 marks)

8

12

Excretion

▷ **Think About:**

1 What waste product is removed from your body by the lungs?

2 Which organ regulates the water content of your body?

3 What is urea?

5 Where is urea made?

6 Where is urea taken out of the blood?

7 Where is urine stored in the body?

8 What does the word 'excretion' mean?

▷ **Waste products**

Humans need to remove from their bodies the chemical wastes that are made in the cells. The two main waste products that have to be removed from the body are:

- **Carbon dioxide** which is produced during respiration. This is removed by the lungs when we breathe out.

- **Urea** which is produced by the liver from the break down of excess amino acids. Urea is filtered out of the blood in the kidneys to form urine and temporarily stored in the bladder.

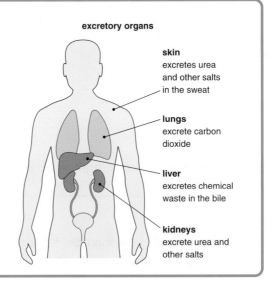

excretory organs

skin
excretes urea and other salts in the sweat

lungs
excrete carbon dioxide

liver
excretes chemical waste in the bile

kidneys
excrete urea and other salts

H

▷ **The urinary system**

The role of the kidneys is to:

- filter urea and other chemical wastes out of the blood;

- control the water content of the body by regulating the amount of water leaving in the urine;

- control the ion content (mainly sodium and chloride ions in salt) of the blood.

Some ions leave in the sweat, but most excess ions leave the body in the urine.

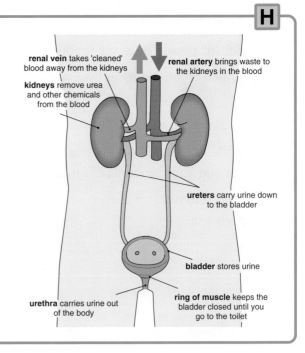

renal vein takes 'cleaned' blood away from the kidneys

renal artery brings waste to the kidneys in the blood

kidneys remove urea and other chemicals from the blood

ureters carry urine down to the bladder

bladder stores urine

urethra carries urine out of the body

ring of muscle keeps the bladder closed until you go to the toilet

Answers: 7. The removal from the body of waste chemicals made in the cells.
1. carbon dioxide 2. the kidneys 3. a waste chemical produced by the break down of excess amino acids 4. the liver 5. the kidneys 6. the bladder

▷ How the kidneys work

Blood is brought to each kidney by the renal artery.
It contains a lot of waste chemicals such as urea.

The renal artery branches many times until the smallest
branches enter tiny filtering units inside the kidney called
nephrons. Here urea (chemical waste), water as well as useful
glucose, amino acids and dissolved ions are filtered out of the
blood into the space inside each nephron.

We can not afford to lose glucose, amino acids, some dissolved
ions and much of the water. Further down the nephron, these
useful materials are re-absorbed back into the bloodstream.

So urea, excess ions and excess water form **urine**, which
passes down each **ureter** to be stored in the **bladder** before
passing out of the body.

Glucose and dissolved ions may each be *actively* re-absorbed
from the nephrons against a concentration gradient. This
requires energy produced by the cells during respiration.

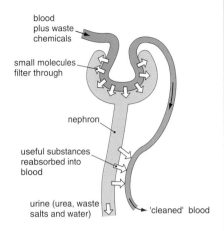

How a nephron works

▷ Controlling body water

If there is too much water in your blood, your kidneys will
produce a lot of dilute urine.
If there is too little water in your blood, your kidneys will
produce a small volume of concentrated urine.

When the water content of the blood is low, a gland in
your brain called the **pituitary**, releases a hormone
called **ADH** into your blood. This causes the kidneys to
re-absorb more water and produces a small amount of
concentrated urine.

When the water content of the blood is too high, the
pituitary releases less ADH into your blood. Less water is
re-absorbed by the kidneys and a larger amount of more
dilute urine is produced.

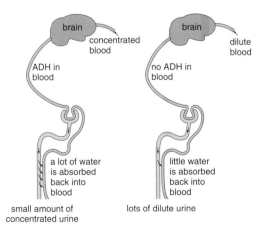

More in *Biology for You*,
pages 111–117.

Take care:

- Do not confuse
  excretion and
  egestion. Excretion
  is getting rid of
  waste chemicals
  made in reactions in the
  cells. Egestion is the removal
  of undigestible food.

- Remember that the
  nephrons in the kidney not
  only filter out waste
  chemicals, they also filter out
  useful chemicals that have to
  be re-absorbed back into the
  blood.

- Follow the diagram of the
  nephron along its length and
  say what happens at each
  stage.

- **Deamination** is a difficult
  concept. If you eat a lot of
  protein then your small
  intestines absorb a lot of
  amino acids. Your body can't
  store these. The liver breaks
  them down to form urea
  which your kidneys excrete.

Examination Questions – Excretion

Year 10 questions

You will need to use the diagram of the human urinary system for questions **1** to **4**.

1 The part labelled 1 is called the …

    A bladder

    B kidney

    C renal artery

    D ureter

2 Urine is stored in the part labelled …

    A 1   **B** 2   **C** 3   **D** 4

3 Blood is filtered in the part labelled …

    A 1   **B** 2   **C** 3   **D** 4

4 This system controls the level of .... in the blood.

    A antibodies   **B** glucose   **C** sugar   **D** water

5 to 8 The kidney helps to maintain the body's internal environment.

5 Which of the following is **not** reabsorbed in the kidney?

    A glucose   **B** mineral ions   **C** urea   **D** water

6 ADH is produced by the …

    A kidney.   **B** liver.   **C** pancreas.   **D** pituitary gland.

7 ADH is produced when …

    A the blood sugar level is too low.   **C** the urea content of the blood is too high.

    B the core temperature is too high.   **D** the water content of the blood is too low.

8 A rise in the level of ADH will result in …

    A the concentration of urine increasing.   **C** the liver producing more urea.

    B the kidneys filtering more blood.   **D** the volume of urine increasing.

9 Substances are filtered from the blood by the kidneys.
   Which **two** of the following substances are actively reabsorbed by the kidneys against a concentration gradient?

    dissolved ions

    insulin

    sugars

    urea

    water

10 Which **one** of the following organs is responsible for the excretion of carbon dioxide?

    A kidney   **B** liver   **C** lungs   **D** skin

Year 11 questions

1 The table shows how much water is lost in different ways from a student's body.

Way in which water is lost	Percentage of total
Breath	15
Faeces	5
Sweat	50
Urine	30

a) Complete the pie chart.

One part has been done for you.
Remember to label the pie chart.

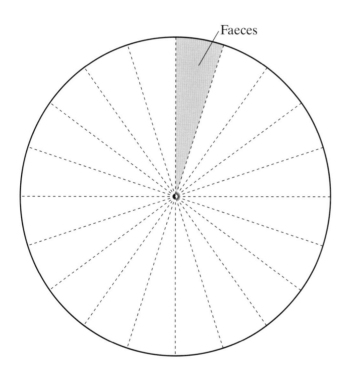

Faeces

(3 marks)

b) The table is about waste products which are removed from the student's body.
Complete the table by using the correct words from the box.

amino acids	breath	circulation	digestion	fatty acids

glucose   respiration   sweat   urine

Waste product	How it is produced	How it leaves the body
carbon dioxide	by	in ....
urea	from...	in ....

(4 marks)   7

Getting the Grades – Maintenance of life

Try this question, then compare your answer with the two examples opposite ▶

1 This question is about how substances get into and out of plants and how they are transported inside the plant.

The diagram shows a section through the leaf of a plant.

a) i Gases enter and leave plants through holes on the lower surface of their leaves. One example is labelled **P** on the diagram opposite.
What are these pores called?

.... [1]

ii Tissue **R** is where most photosynthesis takes place in the leaf.
Cells in tissue **R** need carbon dioxide from the air for this process.
Explain in as much detail as you can, how the gas gets there.

....

....

.... [2]

b) i Why do plants have a cuticle on their leaves?

.... [1]

ii Water vapour can escape through pores in the lower surface of leaves.
Sometimes plants lose water faster than the roots can replace it.
What do guard cells do if this happens?

.... [1]

iii If more water leaves most of the cells in a leaf than enters them:

1 what happens to the pressure inside each of the cells;

....

2 what happens to the leaf?

.... [2]

c) The concentration of nitrate ions in solution around the roots of plants is lower than their concentration in the vacuoles of root hair cells.
Explain in as much detail as you can, how the plant continues to absorb these essential ions.

....

....

....

....

.... [3]

GRADE 'A' ANSWER

1 a) i They are called stomata. ✓

    ii Carbon dioxide diffuses ✓ from the air to the cells in tissue R to allow them to photosynthesise. ✗

b) i To prevent water loss from the leaf. ✓

    ii They close the pore. ✓

    iii 1 The hydrostatic pressure inside the cell decreases. ✓

       2 The leaf wilts. ✓

c) The ions are absorbed against a concentration gradient. ✓ To do this the plant cells use some of the energy ✓ they obtain from respiration. The absorption is brought about by active transport. ✓

This candidate uses precise information and shows comprehensive understanding of this area of the specification. The answer to c) provides a good example.

9 marks = Grade A answer

▶ **Improve your Grades   A up to A***

To get an A* you must complete all parts of the question. There were two marks available in a) ii. The candidate should have made sure that two valid statements were made. This answer restates the question as the second point which makes it invalid.

GRADE 'C' ANSWER

1 a) i Guard cells ✗

    ii It diffuses from the air to the cell. ✓ It does this because there is more in the air than in the cell ✓

b) i To make them waterproof ✓

    ii They close the pores ✓

    iii 1 It drops ✓

       2 It drops ✗

c) The nitrate ions diffuse in by osmosis ✗ because that's he way water gets into a root hair cell. ✗

This question addresses part of the higher tier specification. The candidate might be expected to have realised that the leaf wilts. More precise language would have helped.

This question was targeting part of the higher tier specification. The candidate's answer does not show the necessary knowledge and understanding to be awarded any of the marks on offer.

5 marks = Grade C answer

▶ **Improve your Grades   C up to B**

Learn the work thoroughly and give complete answers to questions. The answer to a) i shows that the candidate had done the work in this part of the specification but the learning was not precise enough.

13

ADAPTATION & COMPETITION

Think About:

1 Name three physical factors that affect organisms.

2 Why do polar bears have a thick coat and lots of body fat?

3 Why do camels have long legs?

4 Why does the cactus have leaves that are small spines?

5 Name two things that plants compete with each other for.

6 What are animals that kill and eat other animals for food called?

▶ Adaptations

> **An adaptation is a feature that enables an organism to survive in its normal habitat.**

Different organisms have to cope with a variety of different conditions, e.g. arid (very dry) deserts, freezing temperatures in the arctic, fast flowing streams or being exposed on the sea shore.

Adaptations may be **special features** like a particular shape of beak for a particular type of seed. They may also be a certain type of **behaviour**, like the way penguins huddle together to keep warm.

Here is a reminder of how two well known animals survive in their extreme habitats:

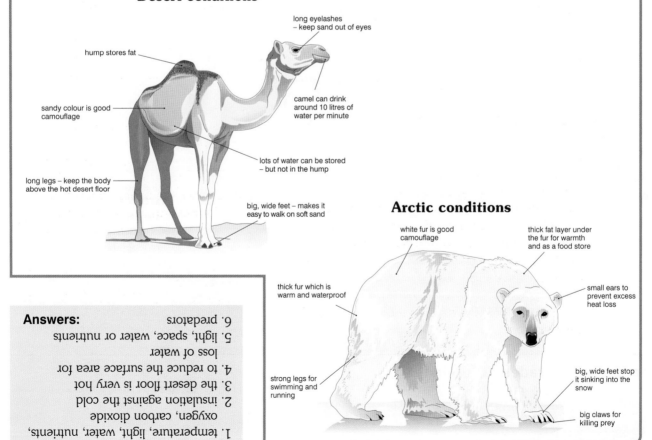

Desert conditions

- long eyelashes – keep sand out of eyes
- hump stores fat
- sandy colour is good camouflage
- camel can drink around 10 litres of water per minute
- lots of water can be stored – but not in the hump
- long legs – keep the body above the hot desert floor
- big, wide feet – makes it easy to walk on soft sand

Arctic conditions

- white fur is good camouflage
- thick fat layer under the fur for warmth and as a food store
- thick fur which is warm and waterproof
- small ears to prevent excess heat loss
- strong legs for swimming and running
- big, wide feet stop it sinking into the snow
- big claws for killing prey

Answers:
1. temperature, light, water, nutrients, oxygen, carbon dioxide
2. insulation against the cold
3. the desert floor is very hot
4. to reduce the surface area for loss of water
5. light, space, water or nutrients
6. predators

▷ Competition

> **In nature competition means animals and plants competing for resources that are in short supply.**

Plants compete with each other for space, light, water and nutrients from the soil.
Animals compete with each other for space, water and food.

If the resources are scarce then only the **best adapted** organisms will survive.
Look at this picture of a weed – it is an excellent competitor because:

- it produces thousands of seeds,
- they germinate quickly in poor soil,
- the plants grow more quickly than those around them,
- they do well in poor soil and harsh conditions.

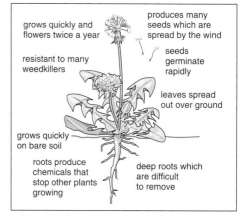

grows quickly and flowers twice a year

produces many seeds which are spread by the wind

resistant to many weedkillers

seeds germinate rapidly

leaves spread out over ground

grows quickly on bare soil

roots produce chemicals that stop other plants growing

deep roots which are difficult to remove

▷ Predation

Predators catch and kill other animals for food. The animals they catch are called their **prey**.

As this graph shows the size of the prey population affects the size of the predator population.

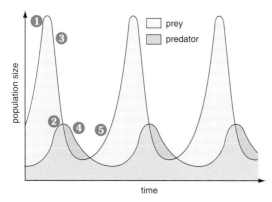

prey
predator

population size

time

- At ❶ the prey population is increasing due to the low level of predation, so many prey are surviving and reproducing.
- At ❷ the predator population is increasing since there is a lot of food (prey) and more predators are surviving and reproducing.
- At ❸, the prey population is decreasing due to increased predation.
- At ❹, the predator population is decreasing due to the lack of prey. Less are surviving and reproducing.
- At ❺, due to lack of predation the prey population is increasing.

More in *Biology for You*, pages 336–343.

▷ Population growth

We must remember that a number of factors affect population sizes not just predators and prey:

- the total amount of food or nutrients available – prey need to eat as well;
- competition for food or nutrients – have you ever seen ducks competing for bread thrown into a pond?
- competition for light – tall plants with lots of leaves will win this competition;
- grazing – sheep are very good at removing shoots from grassland;
- disease – in a large population diseases can spread very quickly.

Take care:

It is not simply the amount of food that makes a population increase. It is because animals are more likely to be able to breed successfully if food is plentiful.

Examination Questions – Adaptation and competition

1   The Arctic fox is a predator that feeds mainly on small mammals. The Arctic fox is adapted to   Marks
    live in the cold conditions of the snow-covered Arctic.

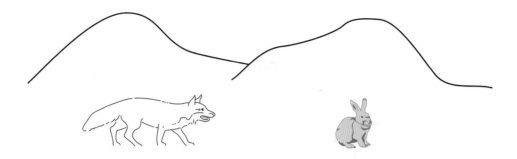

The Arctic fox has thick, white fur.

Give **two** ways in which the fur helps the Arctic fox survive.

1   ....

    ....

2   ....

    ....

                                                                                                (3 marks)   3

2   Long-eared bats are small mammals. They live in woods.

Long-eared bats:
- feed on flying insects at night;
- hibernate during the winter;
- find their food by making high pitched squeaks which reflect off their prey as echoes;
- are caught and eaten by owls.

    a) i Why do these bats need sound to find their prey?

        ....

        ....

                                                                                                (1 mark)

      ii Using information, from the picture, write down one way these bats are adapted for
         finding food using sound.

        ....

        ....

                                                                                                (1 mark)

iii Complete the following sentence.

The bats are prey for owls, so the owls are their ....

(1 mark)

b) Suggest why these bats hibernate in winter.

....

....

(1 mark)

c) The numbers of these bats were counted in a wood every year for 10 years.

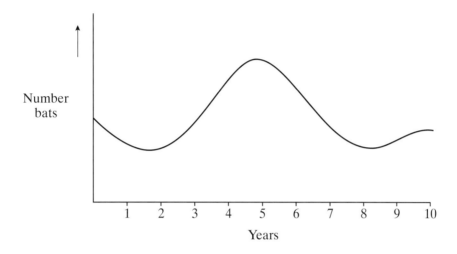

Suggest three reasons for the number of bats increasing between years 2 and 5.

1 ....

....

2 ....

....

3 ....

....

(3 marks)   7

14

ENERGY and BIOMASS

▶ **Think About:**

1 What do we call diagrams showing which organism eats other organisms?

2 What organism do you find at the start of a food chain?

3 What do we call all the other organisms in a food chain?

4 What do we call a group of interconnected food chains?

5 What is transferred from one organism to the next?

6 What does a pyramid of numbers diagram show?

▶ **Energy**

> **The original source of energy for all communities of living organisms is radiation from the sun.**

D

Green plants (especially their leaves) capture this solar energy. It is then transferred into chemical energy and stored in starch and other substances that make up plant cells.

Only about 10% of the solar energy reaching the plant is transferred into chemical energy by photosynthesis.
Look at the drawing of a leaf.
It shows most of the energy:
• is reflected from the leaf,
• passes straight through the leaf,
• simply heats the leaf up.

SUNLIGHT energy

reflected energy

energy warming up the leaf

energy passing straight through

▶ **Biomass**

Biomass is the mass of living material, and as you go along a food chain it gets less and less.

A **pyramid of biomass** shows the mass of all the organisms at each point in a food chain.

Look at this simple food chain:

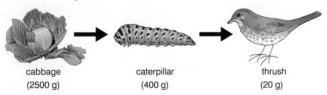

| cabbage (2500 g) | caterpillar (400 g) | thrush (20 g) |

D

We can use these biomass figures to draw a pyramid of biomass to scale.

thrushes

caterpillars

leaves

▷ Food production

If there is less biomass at each stage in a food chain then there must also be less material and less energy.

> **The efficiency of food production can be improved by reducing the number of stages in food chains.**

If we want an energy-efficient diet we should eat from low down the food chain. In other words eating the plants rather than the plant eaters.

H **D**

▷ Energy losses

Why does the biomass at each point in a food chain contain less energy?

Look at the energy gains and losses in this cow:

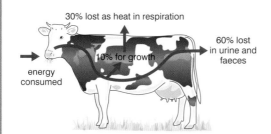

30% lost as heat in respiration

60% lost in urine and faeces

10% for growth

energy consumed

Animals like plants are inefficient at transferring energy.
Only 10% of the energy available to the cow is used for growth.
Of the other 90% some is:

● lost in food that isn't eaten,
● lost in undigested food (faeces) and urine,
● used in respiration.

The cow is a mammal, and mammals like birds must keep their body temperature constant. This results in a lot of energy being lost as heat to their surroundings.

H

▷ More ways to improve the efficiency of food production

Intensive animal farming involves taking steps to reduce energy losses from food animals.

● Animals such as poultry are kept indoors in a temperature-controlled environment.
● Their movement is also restricted to reduce heat loss from respiration, and to ensure that they put weight on quickly.

Plants are treated with hormones.

● These chemicals ensure that they ripen as they appear on supermarket shelves, rather than on the plant or during transport.

You may be asked about the positive and negative effects of managing food production.
The key point is that there has to be a compromise between:

D

> **Maximising food production from the available land, plants and animals, and protecting the environment from damage by pollution or over use and treating animals as humanely as possible.**

Take care:

● It is wrong to say energy is lost from a food chain. It is transferred and most of it ends up as heat.
● Energy is removed from the food chain at each link. The more links there are in the food chain, the more opportunities there are for energy to be removed.

More in **Biology for You**, pages 355–366.

Examination Questions – Energy and biomass

1 The diagram shows the organisms in a food chain. Organism **W** is a green plant.

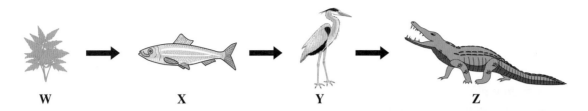

W   X   Y   Z

Marks

   a) Write down **two** things this food chain tells us about organism X.

     1 ....

       ....

     2 ....

       ....

                                                                (2 marks)

   b) Give **one** of the organisms, **W** to **Z**, which is:

     i a predator; ....

     ii a producer. ....   *(2 marks)*   4

2 Lynx feed on hares and grouse.

  The graph shows the changes in population size of these three animals.

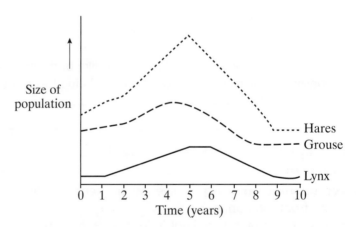

Size of population

Hares
Grouse
Lynx

Time (years)

   a) i Describe how the population of the lynx changes when the numbers of prey increase.

      ....

      ....

                                                       (1 mark)

     ii Suggest why the lynx population decreased after six years.

      ....

      ....

                                                       (1 mark)

   b) The two prey animals feed on the same vegetation.
     If all the lynx were killed by hunters, explain what you would expect to happen to the prey animals and to the vegetation.

     ....

     .... *(2 marks)*

c) Draw a pyramid of biomass for the vegetation, prey and lynx in this community. Label the pyramid.

(1 mark)   5

3 Sand eels are small fish found in the North Sea. The diagram shows the energy transfers between these fish and other organisms.

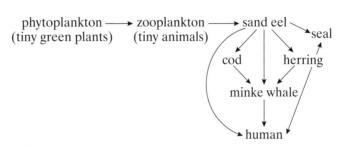

a) What do we call this type of diagram?

.... *(1 mark)*

b) Phytoplankton provide energy for all the animals.
   Explain how phytoplankton can be the energy suppliers.

....

....

....

(3 marks)

c) Humans are removing large numbers of cod and herring from the North Sea.
   Some people say that this will increase the number of sand eels, others say that the number will decrease.
   Both groups of people could be correct. Explain how.

   Why sand eels might increase.

....

....

   Why sand eels might decrease.

....

....

(4 marks)

d) The population of any organism can drop suddenly.
   Give **three** reasons why this could happen.

   1 ....

   2 ....

   3 ....

(3 marks)   11

67

15

Nutrient Cycling

> ## Think About:
>
> 1 What is the scientific word for rotting away?
> 2 What type of organisms are decomposers?
> 3 What are the two most important decomposers?
>
> 4 Where do plants get their nutrients from?
> 5 How do nutrients get into animals?

D

> ## Decomposition
>
> Useful materials like carbon and nitrogen are removed from the environment by living things. Eventually they are returned to the environment in waste materials or as a result of death and decay.
>
> These materials are released when dead organisms are broken down (digested) by **microorganisms**.
> These microorganisms are **bacteria and fungi**.
>
> > **The ideal conditions for decomposition by microorganisms are warm and moist.**
>
> Many bacteria are also more active when there is plenty of **oxygen**.
>
> Look at the diagram:
>
> It shows how, in a stable community, materials are constantly cycled. We can see that decay releases substances that plants need for growth.

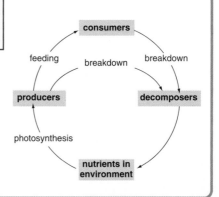

D

> ## Cycling carbon
>
> Carbon is one of the most important elements for living things. They use it to make carbohydrates, proteins, fats and many other molecules.
>
>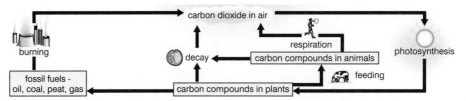
>
> The key points to remember are:
> * **photosynthesis** removes carbon from the atmosphere;
> * **respiration** (in plants, animals and microorganisms) returns some of this carbon to the atmosphere;
> * **burning fossil fuels** also returns carbon to the atmosphere.

D

▷ Making use of decay

Humans use the fact that microorganisms cause decay to:

- break down human waste at sewage works;
- break down plant materials in compost heaps.

> **A compost heap is a place that speeds up natural decomposition.**

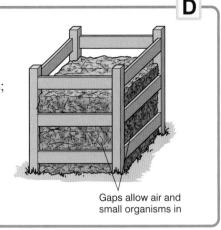

Gaps allow air and small organisms in

▷ Cycling nitrogen

H

D

Plants and animals need nitrogen to produce proteins for growth.

Although about 80% of the atmosphere is nitrogen gas, this is of no use to living things.

> **Nitrogen must be converted into nitrates before plants (and then animals) can use it.**

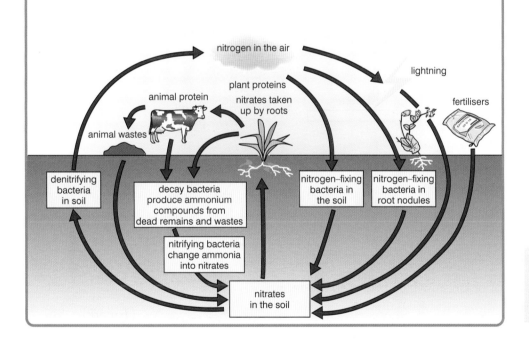

nitrogen in the air

lightning

plant proteins

animal protein

nitrates taken up by roots

fertilisers

animal wastes

denitrifying bacteria in soil

decay bacteria produce ammonium compounds from dead remains and wastes

nitrogen–fixing bacteria in the soil

nitrogen–fixing bacteria in root nodules

nitrifying bacteria change ammonia into nitrates

nitrates in the soil

More in *Biology for You*, pages 369–374.

Take care:

- The nitrogen cycle is harder than the carbon cycle. You need to understand what the different bacteria do.
- Putrefying bacteria break down wastes and dead organisms to form ammonium salts.
- Nitrifying bacteria convert these ammonium salts into nitrates which can be absorbed by the roots of plants and used to make plant protein.
- For the AQA Modular specification, you don't need to know about the action of denitifying or nitrogen-fixing bacteria.

Examination Questions – Nutrient cycling

1 The diagram shows part of the carbon cycle.

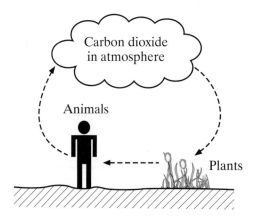

Describe the processes shown in the diagram above.

Marks

....

....

....

....

....

....

(4 marks)

4

2 The diagram shows the cycling of materials in an aquarium.

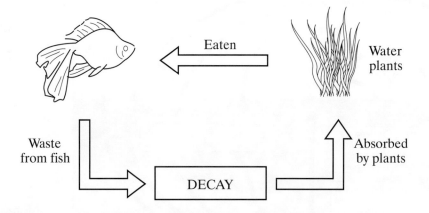

a) Name **one** type of organism which brings about decay.

.... *(1 mark)*

b) i The waste from the fish decays faster if air is continuously bubbled through the water.
Explain why this happens.

....

....

....

(2 marks)

ii Give **one other** factor that affects the rate of decay of waste in the aquarium.

.... *(1 mark)*

4

3 Compost heaps are used to recycle waste plant materials.

Complete the sentences by choosing the correct words from the box.

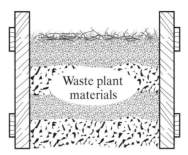
Waste plant materials

cool   decay   dry   grow

moist   respire   warm

The waste plant materials .... because they are broken down by micro-organisms.

The waste plant materials are broken down faster when the conditions are ....
and ....

This process releases substances that can be used by other plants to ....

(4 marks)

4

4 Several processes are involved in the carbon cycle.

The pie chart shows the proportions of these processes.

a) i Calculate the percentage of carbon cycled by respiration.

Percentage .... (1 mark)

Absorbed by oceans 1%
Combustion 4%
Respiration by microbes 5%
Respiration by consumers 21%
Photosynthesis 48%
Respiration by producers 21%

ii One gigatonne is one thousand million tonnes.
Each year, about 165 gigatonnes of carbon is cycled.
Use your answer from i to calculate the mass of carbon cycled by respiration.
Show your working.

Mass of carbon .... gigatonnes (2 marks)

iii Calculate the total percentage of carbon that is removed from the atmosphere each year.

.... (1 mark)

b) What is meant by:

i producer;

....

.... (1 mark)

ii consumer?

....

.... (1 mark)

c) Name the gas which is removed from the atmosphere during photosynthesis.

.... (1 mark)

d) Soil microbes respire.
Give **two** conditions which speed up the activity of soil microbes.

1 ....

2 ....

(2 marks)

9

16

Humans and the environment

▶ Think About:

1 What type of fuels are coal, oil and gas examples of?
2 What do we call chemicals that kill pests?
3 What do we call the place where an animal or plant lives?
4 What do we call it when humans harm their environment?
5 'Normal' rainfall is slightly acidic. What is the gas that makes it so?
6 Why do farmers put fertiliser on their land?

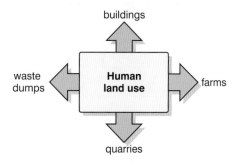

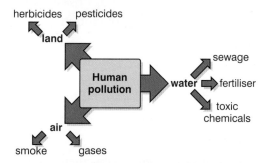

▶ Acid rain

Burning fossil fuels may release **sulphur dioxide** and **nitrogen oxides**. These gases dissolve in rain making it more acidic.

Acid rain can:
- cause trees to lose all their leaves;
- make lakes and rivers so acidic that all aquatic life is killed.

▶ Population growth

As this graph shows the human population has grown rapidly in the last 300 years. This rapid growth is still continuing.
As well as the rise in population, living standards have also increased.
As a result:
- raw materials like non-renewable energy resources are being rapidly used up;
- more waste is being produced;
- if this waste isn't disposed of properly more pollution will be caused.

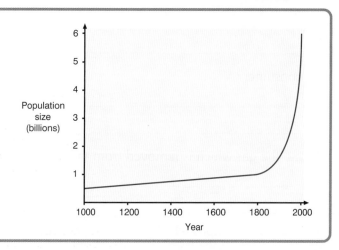

Answers: 1. fossil fuels 2. pesticides 3. habitat 4. pollution 5. carbon dioxide 6. increase crop growth (yield)

▷ The 'greenhouse effect'

The 'greenhouse effect' is the trapping of heat in the Earth's atmosphere due to increasing levels of gases such as **carbon dioxide** and **methane**.

This effect may result in an increase of a few degrees in the Earth's temperature. This is known as **global warming**.

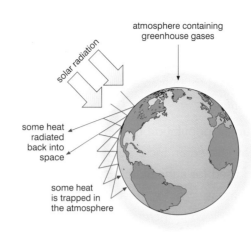

The effects of global warming are being constantly discussed, but they might include:
- a rise in sea level, flooding low-lying land;
- big changes in weather patterns in different parts of the world.

Greenhouse gases are increasing because of:
- increased burning of fossil fuels;
- increased cattle and rice farming (both types of farming release lots of methane).

Large scale **deforestation** provides timber and agricultural land, but:
- it causes more carbon dioxide to be released from burning and the action of microbes;
- less trees means less carbon dioxide removed from the atmosphere by photosynthesis.

▷ Eutrophication

Eutrophication results from excess fertilisers being washed from the soil into lakes and rivers.

The sequence of events is:
- water plants grow rapidly;
- due to competition for light many plants die;
- there is an increase in microorganisms feeding on the dead plants;
- the oxygen level in the water goes down as it is used by the microorganisms in respiration;
- many fish and other aquatic animals die from depletion of oxygen.

Untreated sewage also provides food for microbes and so can also cause eutrophication.

Take care:
- Carbon dioxide and methane are not entirely harmful. Without these gases absorbing heat and re-radiating it back, the Earth would be a much colder place.

- Examiners often ask you 'What can be done?' Think about the following: a) alternative energy sources b) use of unleaded petrol and the greater use of public transport c) use of catalytic converters to reduce emissions of harmful gasses from cars d) stop large scale deforestation because trees absorb carbon dioxide for photosynthesis.

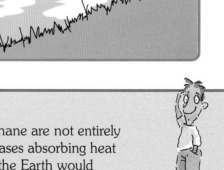

More in *Biology for You*, pages 344–349 and 372.

Examination Questions – Humans and the environment

1 Recently the concentration of carbon dioxide in the Earth's atmosphere has increased slightly. This may be linked to an increase in the 'greenhouse effect'.

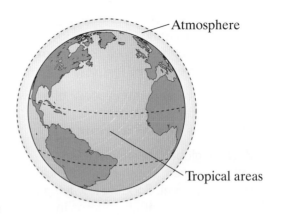
Atmosphere
Tropical areas

a) The human population has grown rapidly. This has caused an increase in the amount of land used for agriculture, especially in tropical areas.
This has helped to increase the carbon dioxide in the atmosphere.
Give **two** reasons for this.

Marks

1 ....

....

2 ....

....

(2 marks)

b) The increased 'greenhouse effect' has caused an increase in the Earth's average temperature.
Give **two** possible environmental effects of this increased average temperature.

1 ....

....

2 ....

....

(2 marks)

c) Name another gas, produced by cattle and rice fields, that also helps cause the 'greenhouse effect'.

....

(1 mark) 5

2 In some countries untreated sewage is allowed to pass directly into rivers.
The diagram shows how some features of a river change when this happens.

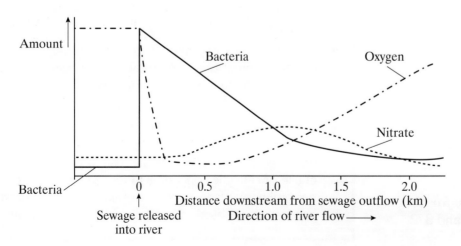

a) Explain why the oxygen content of the water falls at the point where sewage is released into the river.

Marks

....

....

....

....

....

(3 marks)

b) Explain why the nitrate content of the water gradually rises downstream from the sewage outflow.

....

....

....

....

....

(3 marks)

c) Suggest one reason why the oxygen content of the water increases between 1 km and 2 km downstream from the sewage outflow.

....

....

(1 mark) 7

3 People pollute the atmosphere with gases produced by power stations, factories and engines. Some of these gases form acid rain.

The sentences **A–D** are in the wrong order. Write them in the correct order on the flow diagram. (You can just use the letters if you want to.)

A The gases dissolve in rain.

B Fossil fuels are burned.

C Lakes and rivers become acidic so plants and animals die.

D Sulphur dioxide and nitrogen oxides are released.

↓

↓

Gases come out of chimneys and exhausts

↓

↓

Acid rain is produced

↓

(4 marks) 4

75

Getting the Grades – Environment

Try this question, then compare your answer with the two examples opposite ▶

This question considers how humans affect the environment.

1   a) When fossil fuels are burnt carbon dioxide is released into the atmosphere.

        At the same time two other gases are released. These are components of acid rain.

        i Name the **two** gases.

          1 ....   2 .... [2]

        ii Describe **two** ways in which acid rain damages the environment.

          ....

          ....

          ....

          .... [2]

    b) Global demand for timber and the need for agricultural land have led to large scale deforestation in tropical areas.

        How has this affected the concentration of carbon dioxide in the Earth's atmosphere?

        ....

        ....

        ....

        .... [2]

    c) Farmers store grass in silage clamps to feed their livestock in winter.

        Water draining through these dissolves organic molecules and become an extremely polluting waste.

        Describe in as much detail as you can the effect that this waste would have if it got into a small lake.

        ....

        ....

        ....

        ....

        ....

        ....

        ....

        .... [4]

GRADE 'A' ANSWER

This candidate produced a full answer, using precise information and shows comprehensive understanding of this area of the specification. The answers to b) and c) provide good examples

1 a) i 1 sulphur dioxide ✓   2 nitrogen-oxides ✓

    ii Acid rain kills trees. Coniferous trees are particularly sensitive. ✓ This means that the forest will not be as productive. ✗

  b) After the trees are cut down ,the land is cleared. The rubbish is usually burnt. This generates extra carbon dioxide which is added to the atmosphere. ✓ The other thing is that trees are good at removing the carbon dioxide so it means that more goes in and less is taken out ✓

  c) The addition of these organic molecules would result in a dramatic increase in the bacterial population of the lake. ✓ All these bacteria would take oxygen out of the water. (It would increase the BOD) ✓ This would lead to oxygen starvation for the fish ✓ and other aquatic animals. The process is called eutrophication ✓

9 marks = Grade A answer

▶ **Improve your Grades   A up to A***

There were two marks available in a) ii. The candidate should have made sure that two valid descriptions were made. The question asked for '**two** ways' This answer provides only one. The second sentence targets the same marking point and therefore is not rewarded. An A* candidate cannot afford to fail to recognise the significance of the emboldened '**two**'.

GRADE 'C' ANSWER

Answers to a) and b) are basically sound.

1 a) i 1 sulphur dioxide ✓   2 methane ✗

    ii It can damage plants when it rains especially conifer trees. ✓
If it gets into a lake it can make the water to acid for the plants and animals to live in it ✓

  b) After the trees are cut down the rubbish is often burnt and this increases the carbon dioxide in the atmosphere. ✓
There aren't so many trees left to take the gas out of the air ✓

  c) It would make the water very smelly. ✗ Animals that usually drink out of it would probably stop. ✗ Fish would not be able to swim very well. ✗ The stuff might get into their gills and clog them up. ✗

This candidate could not provide clear accurate statements for c). There was evidence of some understanding of problems associated with water pollution in the last statement. The candidate may have remembered that some particulate pollutants do have this effect.

5 marks = Grade C answer

▶ **Improve your Grades   C up to B**

Learn the work thoroughly and give complete answers to questions. The answer to a) i shows that the candidate had done the work in this part of the specification but the learning was not precise enough.

17 Genes and cell division

▷ Think About:
1 What is the name of the male sex cell?
2 What is the name of the female sex cell?
3 What is it called when the male and female sex cells join together?
4 What two things cause the differences in individuals of the same species?
5 Where in a cell is the information for heredity found?

▷ Sexual reproduction

The nucleus of a cell contains **chromosomes** which carry the **genes** that control the characteristics of the body. Many genes have different forms called **alleles** which may produce different characteristics.

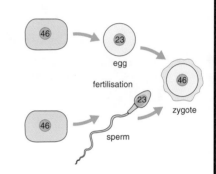

There are two types of reproduction
- **Sexual reproduction** involves the fusion (joining) of male and female **gametes** (sex cells).
- **Asexual reproduction** where there is no fusion of cells and only one individual is needed as the single parent.

Asexual reproduction results in individuals that are genetically identical to the parent and are known as **clones**.

Sexual reproduction results in offspring that have a mixture of genes from each of the two parents. These individuals show more **variation** than offspring produced by asexual reproduction.

H

▷ Cell division

Before a cell divides, a copy of each chromosome is made so that each body cell has exactly the same genetic information. This type of cell division is called **mitosis**.

Mitosis

Cells in human reproductive organs (the testes and ovaries) divide to form gametes. When the cell divides to form gametes:
- copies of chromosomes are made;
- then the cell divides *twice* to form *four* gametes, each with a single set of chromosomes.
This type of cell division is called **meiosis**.

When gametes join at **fertilisation**, a single body cell with *new* pairs of chromosomes is formed. A new individual then develops from this cell repeatedly dividing by mitosis.

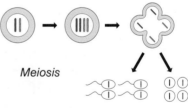

Meiosis

The cells of the offspring produced by asexual reproduction are produced by mitosis from the parental cells. So they contain the *same* genes as the parent.

Sexual reproduction gives rise to variation because:
- the gametes are produced from the parental cells by meiosis;
- when gametes fuse, one of each pair of alleles comes from each parent;
- the alleles in each pair may vary and therefore produce different characteristics.

Answers:

5. the nucleus

1. sperm 2. egg (ovum) 3. fertilisation 4. genes they have inherited (genetic causes) and the conditions in which they have developed (environmental causes)

More in ***Biology for You***, pages 276–277.

The menstrual cycle

 Think About:

1 Where in a woman are the eggs made?
2 What do we call the first stage of adolescence when changes occur in our bodies?
3 What are the chemicals called that bring about these changes?

4 Where are the female hormones produced?
5 What do you think ovulation means?
6 If an egg is not fertilised, then the lining of the uterus breaks down. What do we call this?

 Control of the menstrual cycle

Hormones in a woman control:
- the monthly release of an egg from the woman's ovaries;
- the changes in the thickness of the lining of her uterus (womb).

These hormones are produced by the **pituitary gland** and the **ovaries**.

Fertility in women can be controlled by giving:
- **fertility drugs** which stimulate the ovaries to produce eggs;
- **oral contraceptives** which prevent the release of eggs from the ovaries.

H

 The hormones of the menstrual cycle

- The pituitary produces **FSH** which starts the cycle off. It causes an egg to mature in one of the ovaries. It also stimulates the ovaries to produce hormones which include **oestrogen**.
- Oestrogen is secreted by the ovaries and stops the secretion of FSH by the pituitary, so no more eggs develop. It also causes the lining of the uterus to thicken to receive a fertilised egg, should that happen.
- Oestrogen also gives a signal for the pituitary to secrete another hormone called **LH**.
- LH stimulates the ovary to release an egg (**ovulation**). This occurs at about the middle of the menstrual cycle, when the lining of the uterus is thickened to receive a fertilised egg.

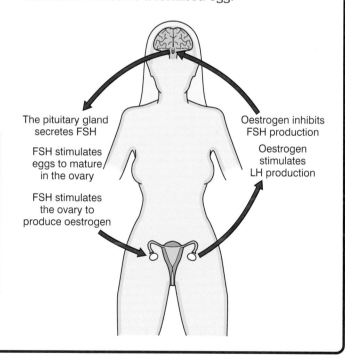

H

 Controlling fertility

- Fertility drugs contain the hormone FSH. If this drug is given to a woman whose own level of FSH is too low, then it can stimulate her ovaries to produce eggs.
- Oral contraceptives contain oestrogen, to inhibit FSH production so no eggs mature to be fertilised.

More in ***Biology for You***, pages 162–163, 167–168.

Answers:
1. the ovaries 2. puberty 3. hormones
4. the ovaries 5. the release of an egg from one of the ovaries
6. a period (menstruation)

Examination Questions – Genes and cell division

1   a) i Name **two** glands which produce hormones that are connected with the monthly (menstrual) cycle in women.

Marks

1 ....

2 ....

(2 marks)

ii Give **two** effects that these hormones have in the body of an adult woman.

1 ....

....

2 ....

....

(2 marks)

b) One method of treating infertility in a woman is to give her hormones.
Suggest the advantages and disadvantages of this method of treating infertility.

....

....

....

....

....

(3 marks)   7

2   The diagram shows some stages in sexual reproduction in a mammal.

Which of the cells, labelled **A–F**:

a) are gametes;   ....

b) have chromosomes in pairs;   ....

c) divide by meiosis;   ....

d) have identical genetic information? .... *(4 marks)*   4

3 Some gardeners have a lot of trouble with a weed called couch grass.

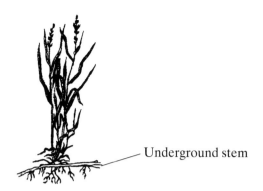

Underground stem

When they pull the plant up, small pieces of underground stems are left in the soil.

The cells of each piece produce a new plant.

Growth occurs by mitosis. The diagram shows the first two stages involved.

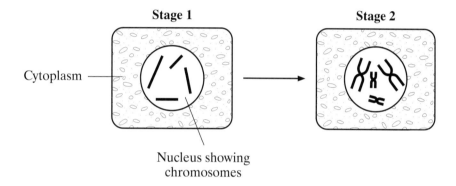

a) Describe what has happened to the chromosomes between stages 1 and 2.

....

(1 mark)

b) Draw the chromosomes which would be in each of the two new cells by the end of mitosis.

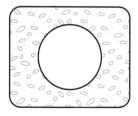 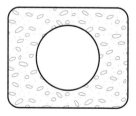

(2 marks)

c) Couch grass plants have a pair of genes which control stem length.
   These genes exist as the alleles **A** or **a**. A parent plant is **Aa**. What alleles will the new plants have if they are produced by mitosis?

....

(1 mark)

4

18 Artificial selection and genetic engineering

▷ **Think About:**

1 What do you call offspring that are genetically identical to the parent?
2 How has cloning been useful to the commercial production of plants?
3 What is meant by selective breeding?
4 What useful characteristics have been 'bred into' sheep?
5 What useful characteristics have been 'bred into' modern wheat varieties?

▷ Cloning

New plants can be produced quickly and cheaply by taking **cuttings** from older plants. The new plants are genetically identical to the parent plant and so retain any useful characteristics e.g. flower colour, scent and number of flowers. Cuttings are most likely to grow successfully if grown in a damp atmosphere until roots develop.

Modern cloning techniques include :

- **tissue culture** – using small groups of cells from part of a plant;
- **embryo transplants** – splitting apart cells from a developing animal embryo before they become specialised, then transplanting the identical embryos into host mothers (surrogates).

A disadvantage of cloning is that its widespread use in agriculture reduces the number of alleles available for selective breeding.

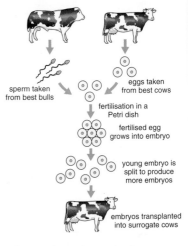

sperm taken from best bulls

eggs taken from best cows

fertilisation in a Petri dish

fertilised egg grows into embryo

young embryo is split to produce more embryos

embryos transplanted into surrogate cows

Stages in embryo cloning

▷ Artificial selection

Artificial selection and selective breeding mean the same thing. It involves choosing individuals which have characteristics useful to humans and breeding from them. So we can use artificial selection to produce new varieties of organisms.

For example, cattle have been selectively bred for:

- quantity and quality of their meat. These breeds include the Hereford and Aberdeen Angus.
- milk yield. These breeds include Jersey and Guernsey cattle.

In a similar way, Merino sheep have been selectively bred for their wool. Down sheep, on the other hand, have been selectively bred for their meat.

> **Artificial selection is the breeding of plants and animals to create characteristics useful to humans.**

But the disadvantages of selective breeding are :

- it greatly reduces the number of alleles and therefore the genetic variation in a population;
- further selective breeding to enable the species to survive changed conditions may not then be possible.

A Hereford calf

A Merino sheep

▷ Genetic engineering

Many diseases are caused when the body can not make a particular protein. For instance diabetics can not make insulin. Genetic engineering can be used to make large amounts of these proteins.

> **Genetic engineering means transferring genes from one type of cell to another.**

Genes carry all the instructions for how your body works. The technique used in genetic engineering is to get the cells of **microbes** to make the useful chemicals.

- First the human gene that codes for the useful chemical (e.g. insulin) is identified.
- Special enzymes are used as 'chemical scissors' to cut out the useful gene from the rest of the DNA.
- A circular piece of DNA, called a **plasmid**, is removed from a bacterium.
- The human gene is inserted into the plasmid and the plasmid put back into a bacterium.
- The bacterial cells multiply very rapidly in a fermenter. They make exact copies of themselves and the human gene. So lots of the useful chemical, like insulin, is produced.

The advantages of this technique in insulin production are that the insulin is identical to human insulin (so no side-effects), it is made in large quantities and is cheap to produce.

Genes can also be transferred to the cells of animals or plants at an early stage of development so that they develop with the desired characteristics.

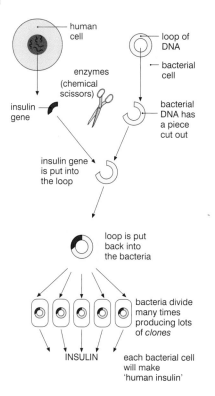

Take care:

- Artificial selection and selective breeding are different terms for the same thing: the breeding of plants and animals to produce characteristics that are useful to humans.

- Cloning is a form of asexual reproduction needing only one parent. The offspring are genetically identical to that parent.

- Genetic engineering involves transferring genetic material from one species to another. There are economic, social and ethical issues concerning both cloning and genetic engineering. You need to be aware of the arguments for and against these techniques.

More in *Biology for You*, pages 289–293.

Answers: 1. clones 2. Plants can be produced quickly and cheaply with all the good characteristics of the parent plant.
3. Breeding in the characteristics that we want and breeding out the characteristics that we don't want.
4. quality of wool and meat 5. greater yield, improved resistance to disease and shorter ripening time

Examination Questions – Artificial selection and genetic engineering

1 When potato chips are fried, much of the water in the potato cells is replaced by fat.

Scientists have used genetic engineering to produce a new variety of potato that contains reduced amounts of water.

Give arguments for and against using genetic engineering to produce new varieties of potato.

....

....

....

....

....

....

....

....

....

(4 marks)   4

2 Mussels are a type of shellfish. They cling to rocks on the seashore using strong threads. The threads are stuck to the rocks by a waterproof protein glue. This is much stronger than most man-made glues.

A gene in the mussel stores the information for making the glue.

Scientists are hoping to genetically engineer plants to make the glue in large quantities.

a) Describe how the information for making the glue is stored in the gene and how this information is used to make the protein glue.

....

....

....

....

....

(4 marks)

b) Describe how genetic engineering could be used to make plants that produce the glue.

....

....

....

....

(3 marks)   7

3 The photograph shows a variety of horse used for farm work.

a) Explain what is meant by artificial selection.

....

....

....

....

(2 marks)

b) Suggest how farmers used artificial selection to produce this variety of horse. Use information from the photograph to help you.

....

....

....

....

(2 marks)   4

19

▷ **Think About:**

1 What do we mean by the word 'extinction'?

2 Can you name any animals that are extinct?

3 What is a fossil?

4 How are fossils preserved?

5 What do we mean by the word 'evolution'?

▷ **Fossils**

> **Fossils are the preserved remains of animals and plants from millions of years ago.**

Fossils can be formed in a number of ways:

- The hard parts of animals do not decay easily. Bones, teeth and scales may get buried by sediment which turns to rock. The hard parts become replaced by minerals giving an exact copy.
- Soft parts can form fossils if decay is slow. They can be replaced with hard minerals which take on exactly the same shape.
- If conditions for decay are absent then the plant or animal may be preserved e.g. if buried in peat bogs or in the ice.

Fossils are able to give scientists information about how much different organisms have changed since life developed on Earth. Preserved traces of animals or plants, e.g. footprints, burrows or rootlet traces also provide valuable information.

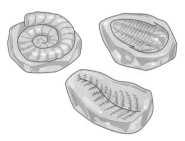

Which living things do these fossils most resemble?

▷ **Mutations**

> **Mutations are new forms of genes resulting from changes in existing genes.**

Mutation can occur naturally, but the chance of mutations occurring is increased by:

- Exposure to ionising radiation e.g. ultraviolet light, X-rays and radiation from radioactive substances. The greater the dose of radiation, the greater the chance of mutation.
- Certain chemicals.

*This man is an **albino** and the condition is caused by a mutation.*

Answers: 1. When a species, that once inhabited the Earth, dies out. 2. Dodo, Tasmanian wolf, wood bison, giant otter etc. 3. remains of plants or animals from millions of years ago 4. trapped in sediments when their parts are replaced with hard minerals, trapped in ice or in peat bogs where decay is prevented 5. The gradual change in the characteristics of a species.

86

▷ Evolution

> **Evolution is the gradual change in the characteristics of a species over time.**

The theory of evolution states that all species of living things which exist today (and many more which are now extinct) have evolved from simple life-forms which first developed more than three billion years ago.

Charles Darwin's theory of evolution by **natural selection** was only gradually accepted by other scientists. Modern knowledge about genes has resulted in an up-dating of Darwin's theory of natural selection as follows:

- Organisms produce large numbers of offspring.

- In any particular species there is variation between individuals, because of differences in their genes.

- Predation, disease and competition cause many individuals to die.
  There is a 'struggle for existence' between individuals of the same species.

- Individuals with characteristics most suited to their environment are more likely to survive and breed.
  This is often called 'the survival of the fittest'.

- The genes that have enabled these individuals to survive are then passed on to their offspring.

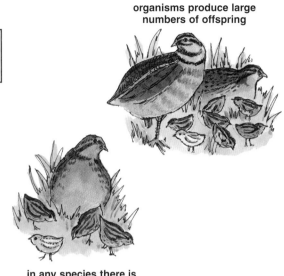
organisms produce large numbers of offspring

in any species there is variation between individuals

there is a struggle for existence

organisms with useful characteristics are more likely to survive and pass them on to the next generation

▷ Extinction

Since life on Earth began, many species have become **extinct**.

This may have been due to changes in the environment, such as climate, or the appearance of new predators, new diseases or new competitors. Unless evolution occurs and species become better adapted to survive these changes they may become extinct.

Most mutations are harmful and can result in uncontrolled cell divisions of body cells. These are **cancers**. But some mutations are neutral in their effects and may increase the chances of survival of an organism and any offspring that inherit the mutant gene.

More in **Biology for You**, pages 285, 296–307.

Take care:
- Not all mutations are harmful, some may increase an organism's chances of survival. Without mutations, evolution could not occur.

- When answering questions on natural selection, remember to say *how* particular characteristics of an organism have enabled it to survive.

Examination Questions – Evolution and natural selection

1 The drawing shows *Hyracotherium*. Fossils of this animal have been found. It looked rather like a small horse. It lived about 60 million years ago.

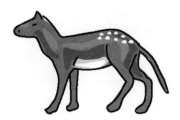

a) Describe how fossils of this animal might have been formed.

....

....

....

....

(2 marks)

b) Explain how evidence from studying fossils supports the theory of evolution.

....

....

....

....

....

(3 marks)

c) There was another horse-like mammal living 60 million years ago. **Diagram A** shows the bones in one of its feet. This type of foot is suitable for running on marshy ground.

A modern horse has a foot like the one in **Diagram B** below. This type of foot is more suitable for running on firm ground.

**Diagram
A**

**Diagram
B**

Explain how the feet of the modern horse might have evolved from the feet of the horse-like mammal that lived 60 million years ago.

....

....

....

....

....

....

....

....

(4 marks)　　9

2　A scientist called Lamarck proposed a theory of evolution. The passage gives Lamarck's explanation of the evolution of the long legs of wading birds.

Change occurs because an animal passes on to its offspring changes it acquires during its lifetime. The long legs of wading birds arose when those animals' ancestors responded to a need to feed on fish. In their attempt to get into deeper water, but still keep their bodies dry, they would stretch their legs to the full extent, making them slightly longer in the process. This trait would be passed on to the next generation, who would in turn stretch their legs. Over many generations, the wading birds' legs became much longer.

Darwin's theory of natural selection would give a different explanation for the evolution of the long legs of wading birds.

Describe the difference between Lamarck's and Darwin's explanations of the evolution of the long legs of wading birds.

....

....

....

....

....

....

....

....

(4 marks)　　4

20

▷ **Think About:**

1 Where are your genes found?
2 What are chromosomes?
3 How many chromosomes are there in most human cells?

4 Which cells have half the normal chromosome number?
5 What is the chemical that genes are made of?

▷ Chromosomes and alleles

In human body cells there are 23 pairs of chromosomes (46 in total).
The last pair of chromosomes are called the **sex chromosomes**.
They determine whether you are a boy or a girl.
In females the sex chromosomes look the same (XX). But in males there is one long X chromosome and one much shorter Y chromosome, so a male has XY sex chromosomes. It depends whether the mother's egg is fertilised by an X or Y sperm whether you turn out a boy or a girl.

Chromosomes are thread-like structures and are made up of protein and long molecules of a chemical called **DNA**.
A gene is a small section of DNA that codes for a particular character.
For certain characteristics, the characteristic is controlled by one gene. But some genes have two different forms called **alleles**.

An allele which controls the development of a characteristic when it is present on only one of the chromosomes is a **dominant** allele.
An allele which controls the development of characteristics only if the dominant allele is not present is a **recessive** allele.

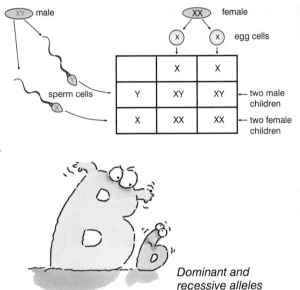

Dominant and recessive alleles

▷ Hereditary diseases

Some human disorders are inherited.

- **Huntington's disease** is a disorder of the nervous system. It is caused by a dominant allele of a gene, so that it can be passed on by only one parent who has the disorder.
- **Cystic fibrosis** is a disorder of the cell membranes. It is caused by a recessive allele, so has to be inherited from *both* parents. The parents may be **carriers** of the disorder without actually suffering from the disease themselves.
- **Sickle-cell anaemia** is a disorder of the red blood cells which reduces the ability of the blood to carry oxygen. It is caused by a recessive allele, so that a sufferer will have inherited a recessive allele from *each* carrier parent.

Answers:

1. inside the nucleus of cells   2. thread-like structures made up of DNA and protein
3. 46(23 pairs)   4. the gametes (sperm and egg cells)   5. DNA

90

▷ Genetic crosses

We can predict and explain the outcomes of crosses between individuals.

If *both* chromosomes in a pair contain the same allele of a gene, then the individual is **homozygous** for that gene e.g. AA or aa.

If the chromosomes in a pair contain *different* alleles of a gene, then the individual is **heterozygous** for that gene e.g. Aa.

There are two alleles for flower colour. **R** codes for red and **r** codes for white.

Here is a cross between a homozygous red flowered plant and a white flowered plant.

The offspring are heterozygous red flowered and if we cross these the result is 3 red to 1 white.

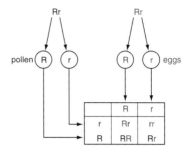

You can use a Punnett square to show how two carriers of cystic fibrosis can produce a child with cystic fibrosis:

With this cross you can see how only one parent with Huntington's disease is able to pass on the condition:

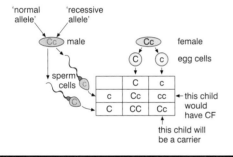
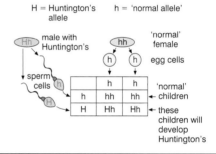

▷ DNA

A DNA molecule contains coded information that determines inherited characteristics. DNA is made up of very long strands which have *four* different compounds called **bases**.

You know that proteins are made up of amino acids bonded together. A sequence of *three* bases is the code for a particular amino acid. So the order of bases in the DNA molecule controls the order in which amino acids are assembled to produce a particular protein.

The DNA molecule looks like a spiral staircase

Take care:

- The chances of having a boy (or of having a girl) are 50:50. So if the first child is a girl there is still a 50:50 chance of the next child being a girl.

- When showing genetic crosses, we always use a capital letter to represent the dominant allele (e.g. D) and a lower case letter (e.g. d) to represent the recessive allele.

- Carrier individuals do not suffer from a genetic disease e.g. cystic fibrosis. They are heterozygous and carry the recessive allele for the condition which they *could* pass on to their offspring.

- Genetic questions have a language of their own, so be clear on what is meant by dominant, recessive, homozygous and heterozygous.

More in *Biology for You*, pages 272–288.

Examination Questions – Genetics

1 Complete each sentence by choosing the correct terms from the box.

23	**46**	**ADH**	**DNA**	**XX**	**XY**	**YY**	
dominant	**female**	**male**	**recessive**	**strong**	**weak**		

A gene is made up of a substance called .... Genes are found on chromosomes

and most human cells contain .... pairs of chromosomes. In females the two sex

chromosomes are .... , but in males the two sex chromosomes are ....

Alleles are alternative forms of a gene. Two healthy parents can sometimes have a child with

a genetic disorder such as cystic fibrosis. This is because cystic fibrosis is caused by a

.... allele. The two parents are healthy because they also have the

.... allele. *(6 marks)*   6

2 a) Use words from the list to complete the sentences about inheritance.

   cells   genes   nuclei   sperm

   A father and his son look similar. They both have the same colour hair and

   eyes and the same shape of nose. This is because .... that control the son's

   characteristics were passed on by his father in his .... *(2 marks)*

   b) Give **one** reason why the son's characteristics would not all be the same as the father's.

   ....

   ....

   (1 mark)   3

3 In 1993, scientists produced a sheep called Tracey. When Tracey was just an embryo, the
scientists transferred a human gene into her cells. When Tracey became an adult, she was able
to produce milk that contained a protein called AAT. This substance is used to treat people
who suffer from cystic fibrosis. Tracey gave birth to two lambs. Both these lambs were able to
produce AAT.

   a) The human gene transferred into Tracey is part of a DNA molecule.
      Describe the structure of a DNA molecule.

   ....

   ....

   ....

   ....

   (2 marks)

b) AAT is a protein. Describe the role of DNA in producing proteins.

Marks

....

....

....

....

(2 marks)

c) Give arguments for **and** against transferring human genes into animals.

....

....

....

....

....

....

(3 marks)

7

4 Cystic fibrosis is an inherited disease.

- It is partly due to a faulty allele **n**. People with two faulty alleles suffer from the disease.
- People with just one normal allele **N** do not suffer from the disease.

a) What do we call people who do not suffer from a disease but can pass it on to their children?

....

(1 mark)

b) Draw a genetic diagram to show what can happen when two **Nn** parents have children. Show on the diagram which of the children have the disease.

(3 marks)

c) The faulty allele was caused by a normal gene being changed.

  i What are changes in genes called?

....

(1 mark)

  ii Name **two** different factors which may cause changes in genes.

....

....

(3 marks)

7

Getting the Grades – Inheritance and selection

Try this question, then compare your answer with the two examples opposite ▶

1   a) Complete the following sentences.

      i The number of chromosomes found in the nucleus of a human body cell is

      ....

      ii The sex chromosomes of the human female are represented by ....

      and those of the male by ....

      iii Chromosomes have long molecules of a substance called ....

      iv Different forms of the same gene are called ....   [5]

   b) i Name an inherited disorder of the nervous system.

      .... [1]

      ii Cystic fibrosis is an inherited disorder of cell membranes.

      Cystic fibrosis is caused by a recessive allele of a gene.

      Explain how two healthy parents can have a child that has cystic fibrosis.

      You can use a genetic diagram to help if you wish to.

      ....

      ....

      ....

      .... [4]

GRADE 'A' ANSWER

This candidate produced a full answer (except for b)i), using precise information and shows comprehensive understanding of this area of the specification. The omission was probably a result of carelessness stemming from the candidate's haste to get on to a piece of work they obviously knew well. The answers to b)ii provides a good example. There were several points made which could have been awarded marks but were not because the maximum had been reached. For example, referring to the parents as 'carriers' or reference to the fact that there is a 1 in 4 chance of any of the offspring having two recessive alleles are credit worthy statements..

1 a) i 23 pairs (46) ✓
　　 ii XX ✓ and XY ✓
　　 iii DNA ✓
　　 iv alleles ✓
　 b) i ✗
　　 ii Let the normal, healthy allele be represented by 'C'.
　　　 Let the recessive allele be represented by 'c'.
　　　 The parents have to be carriers. They are heterozygous,
　　　 'Cc'.
　　　 50% of the man's sperm would have 'C' and 50% 'c'.
　　　 The same would be true for the woman's eggs, 50:50
　　　 'C' and 'c'. ✓
　　　 The possible pairing of alleles at fertilisation can be
　　　 seen in a diagram.

gametes	C	c
C	CC	Cc
c	Cc	cc

This shows that the couple could have a child with cystic fibrosis. There is a 1 in 4 chance of the recessive alleles, 'cc' being brought together at fertilisation.

9 marks = Grade A answer

▶ **Improve your Grades   A up to A***

An A* candidate will be expected to attempt all sections of the paper. The standard of the rest of the answer would suggest that this candidate was at the appropriate level. Perhaps this candidate failed to read through the paper before the end of the examination when they would have spotted this 'careless' gap.

GRADE 'C' ANSWER

The response to this is too vague. No attempt is made to provide a genetic diagram. The first statement shows a common misunderstanding. The candidate does not provide any evidence of the knowledge and understanding necessary to be awarded any of the marks on offer here.

1 a) i 23 pairs ✓
　　 ii XX ✓ and XY ✓
　　 iii DNA ✓
　　 iv homozygotes ✗
　 b) i Huntington's disease ✓
　　 ii This is because the one gene is weaker than the
　　　 other. ✗
　　　 So the parents don't have it much and it doesn't
　　　 show up. ✗
　　　 But when it gets together in the baby its much
　　　 worse. ✗
　　 ✗

5 marks = Grade C answer

▶ **Improve your Grades   C up to B**

Learn the work thoroughly taking care to use scientific terms correctly. Take guidance from the question wherever you can. The examiner has given a prompt in b) ii in the last sentence of the question.

21 Movement and feeding

▶ Think About:

1 What are the three functions of the skeleton?
2 What do we call the place where bones meet?
3 Muscles working as a pair are known as what?
4 What is the digestive juice in the mouth called?

5 Mechanical digestion involves what structures?
6 Name the four different kinds of teeth.

▶ The skeleton and movement

> **The skeleton allows movement when muscles contract to move bones at joints.**

The main structures in a joint are:
- **ligaments** that hold bones together, they are strong and slightly elastic;
- smooth **cartilage** that stops bones rubbing together and absorbs shocks;
- **tendons** attach muscles to bones, these are strong and inelastic;
- **synovial membrane** which **secretes synovial fluid** lubricating the joint.

▶ Exercise

*Regular exercise is **good** for you as it:*
- keeps muscle fibres slightly tensed, ready to contract (this is called **muscle tone**);
- increases muscle strength and avoids stiffness and soreness after exercise;
- keeps joints working smoothly;
- maintains an efficient blood supply to the muscles, heart and lungs.

*Exercise is **bad** for you if:*
- ligaments are torn by a sudden wrench – this is a **sprain**;
- a bone is forced out of a joint – this is a **dislocation**.

▶ Movement in fish

Fish are well adapted to swimming by having:
- a zig-zag muscle arrangement,
- a large tail fin that pushes against the water,
- a streamlined body shape.

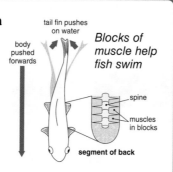

tail fin pushes on water
body pushed forwards
Blocks of muscle help fish swim
spine
muscles in blocks
segment of back

H

Fish also have:
- a gas-filled **swim bladder** for buoyancy;
- dorsal and ventral fins to keep it upright;
- paired fins for up, down and backwards movement.

▶ Movement in birds

Birds are adapted for flight by having:
- wings with a large surface area that push downwards on the air for lift;
- strong and light flight feathers;
- honey comb structure bones that are strong but light;
- a streamlined body shape.

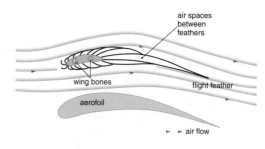

air spaces between feathers
wing bones
flight feather
aerofoil
► ► air flow

H

Flight in birds is assisted by:
- the **aerofoil** wing shape which creates lower pressure above the wing giving lift;
- flight feathers interlocking to give a smooth surface;
- primary and secondary feathers that give lift and forward propulsion.

Answers:
1. support, movement and protection
2. joint 3. antagonistic 4. saliva
5. teeth 6. incisors, canines, premolars and molars

▶ Invertebrate feeding

> **Invertebrates often feed by using a filtering or a sucking action.**

Mussels are filter feeders, they feed on microscopic water organisms (plankton):
- water is drawn through their body by beating **cilia**;
- gills sieve out the plankton;
- other cilia move this plankton to the mouth.

Mosquitoes feed by sucking blood:
- they pierce skin and blood capillaries with a sharp needle-like **proboscis**;
- they secrete saliva containing an anti-clotting agent into the capillary;
- their throat muscles help to draw blood up the proboscis.

Other invertebrates that feed by sucking fluids are: aphids, butterflies and houseflies.

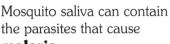

H

Mosquito saliva can contain the parasites that cause **malaria**.

This parasite is a single celled organism which feeds and reproduces inside human red blood cells. When these cells rupture it causes a severe fever.

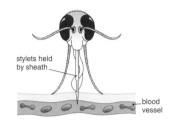

stylets held by sheath

blood vessel

▶ Adaptations to feeding in mammals

> **Mammals use teeth to help feeding and their shape is suited to their function.**

In humans the **incisors** and **canines** are the biting teeth and the **premolars** and **molars** are the chewing teeth.

Dog teeth are adapted for a meat-based diet:
- small chisel-like incisors pull meat apart;
- sharp pointed canines grip prey and tear meat apart;
- premolars and molars include the **carnassial** teeth that shear meat and crush bones;
- the up and down jaw action acts like a pair of scissors.

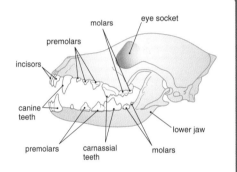

molars — eye socket
premolars
incisors
canine teeth
lower jaw
premolars — carnassial teeth — molars

H

▶ The digestive system of mammals is also adapted to their diet. Herbivorous animals like cows and sheep eat a lot of **cellulose**. Mammals do not have a cellulose-digesting enzyme. Much of it is broken down by bacteria in the gut. Cows and sheep have these bacteria in a **rumen** between the oesophagus and stomach. They also re-chew part-digested food.

Rabbits have their cellulose bacteria in the **caecum** between the small and large intestine. To aid digestion rabbits often eat their own faeces.

The bacteria and the herbivores enjoy a **mutualistic** relationship – they both benefit.

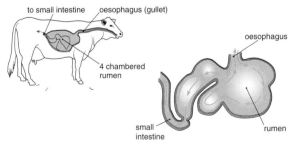

to small intestine — oesophagus (gullet)
4 chambered rumen
oesophagus
small intestine
rumen

The stomach of ruminants has a special bacteria-containing chamber called the rumen

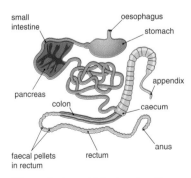

small intestine
oesophagus
stomach
appendix
pancreas
colon
caecum
faecal pellets in rectum
rectum
anus

The gut of a rabbit showing the enlarged caecum that contains cellulose-digesting bacteria

More in *Biology for You*, pages 62–65 and 146–149.

Examination Questions – Movement and feeding

1 Fish are adapted for movement in water.

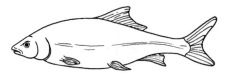

a) Describe and explain how the shape of the fish adapts it for movement in water.

Marks

....

....

....

(2 marks)

b) Label the diagram.

   1 Label with the letter A, a fin that provides most of the forward thrust in swimming.

   2 Label with the letter B, a fin that allows the fish to move up in the water.

(2 marks)

c) Why does a fish not sink to the bottom when it stops swimming?

....

....

(1 mark)

5

2 The diagram show the arrangement of structures in a hip joint.

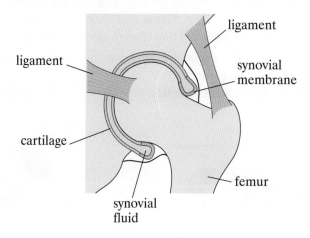

Complete the table opposite to summarise the properties of skeletal tissues that adapt them for their functions.

Tissue	Properties	Function
bone	hard	
ligament		Keeps the joint together but allows it to bend without easily dislocating
cartilage		
tendon	Has tensile strength and little elasticity	

(5 marks)   5

3   a) Describe in as much detail as you can, how mosquitoes feed.

....

....

....

....

....

(4 marks)

b) The diagram shows the skull of a sheep. This animal is a herbivore.

Describe how the dentition and skull of a carnivore, such as a dog, would differ from the dentition and skull of the sheep.

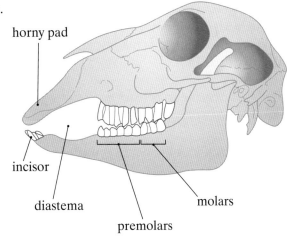

Dentition

....

....

....

(5 marks)

Skull

....

....

....

(1 mark)   10

CONTROLLING

DISEASE

▶ Think About:

1 What are the main disease-causing microorganisms?

2 What causes the symptoms of a disease?

3 What type of microorganism causes (i) tuberculosis, (ii) measles, (iii) athletes foot?

4 What drugs kill bacteria?

5 When you catch a disease but then don't get it again you are said to be what?

▶ Controlling infectious disease

> **Microorganisms that cause disease are known as pathogens.**

Medicines contain useful drugs, but some of them like painkillers only relieve the symptoms rather than killing the pathogens.

Antibiotics such as penicillin do kill bacteria but they cannot kill viruses.

Viruses live and reproduce inside living cells. They are difficult to kill without damaging living tissue.

Bacteria can become resistant to antibiotics, therefore:
- the most effective antibiotic for each infection must be chosen, and
- to avoid further resistance antibiotics must not be over used

Active immunity involves:
- an injection of dead or weakened pathogens;
- these have **antigens** on their surface;
- the antigens stimulate white blood cells to produce **antibodies**;
- these destroy the antigens.
- e.g. the MMR vaccine to protect against measles, mumps and rubella.

Passive immunity involves:
- an injection of antibodies rather than the pathogens themselves;
- this is done if a person has already been exposed to a dangerous pathogen, e.g. injecting rabies antibodies if a person has been bitten by a dog that might have rabies.

In both cases the injection is known as a **vaccination**.

▶ How does the immune response work?

There are two kinds of white blood cell (lymphocytes) involved.
- **T-cells** have surface receptors that recognise and attach to antigens.
- They then destroy them.
- T-cells stimulate **B-cells** to multiply.
- B-cells secrete antibodies specific to a particular antigen.
- Memory cells remain in the body ensuring a rapid response to future infections.

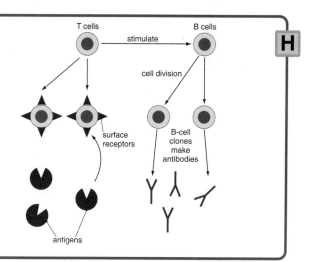

H

Answers:
1. bacteria and viruses 2. chemicals released by the microorganisms 3. (i) bacteria (ii) virus (iii) fungi 4. antibiotics 5. immune

▶ Treating kidney disease

> **If untreated, kidney disease will cause death due to a build up of toxic substances in the blood.**

Kidney failure can either be treated by **dialysis** or by a **transplant**.

Dialysis has to be carried out *every few days.*
The patient's blood flows between two partially permeable membranes and the waste **urea** passes out into the dialysis fluid.

H

▶ How does the dialysis machine work?

The dialysis fluid contains the same concentration of useful substances as blood plasma. These useful substances include **glucose** and **mineral ions**. As a result it is only the urea and any excess ions that pass out of the blood by **diffusion**.

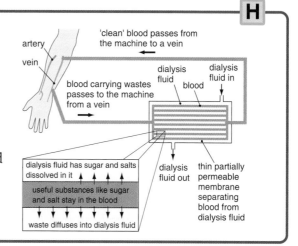

H

▶ Transfusions

Also if a blood transfusion is needed during the operation this blood must be matched with the recipients own blood.
The main blood groups are A, B, AB and O.
In this system there are: **antigens** on the surface of the red blood cells and **antibodies** in the plasma.
These antibodies do not attack antigens on their own red blood cells.

This **compatibility table** shows which groups are safe for transfusion:

Group	Can donate to	Can receive from
A	A and AB	A and O
B	B and AB	B and O
AB	AB	all groups
O	all groups	O

▶ Kidney transplants

> **A healthy kidney from a donor might be rejected by the immune system of the recipient.**

To prevent rejection:
- the donor kidney must have a similar **'tissue type'** to the recipient;
- the recipient's bone marrow is treated with radiation to stop white cell production;
- the recipient is kept in sterile conditions for some time after the operation;
- the recipient takes drugs to suppress the immune system.

More in **Biology for You**, pages 179–182, 103 and 115.

Take care:
- Do not confuse antigens and antibodies.
- Antigens are chemicals found on **cell surfaces** and antibodies are chemicals that the body makes in **response** to them.

Examination Questions – Controlling disease

1 Complete the sentences by choosing the correct words form the list.

Marks

active	**antibodies**	**antigens**	**passive**
pathogen	**platelets**	**red**	**white**

Someone can be protected against a disease by having small quantities of dead or inactive forms of a pathogen, in a vaccine, introduced into their blood stream. .... in the vaccine stimulate .... blood cells to produce .... This makes a person immune to future infections by the .... This is called .... immunity.

(5 marks)

5

2 Read the passage about antibiotics.

People do not always agree about the use of antibiotics in food production.

If we put low doses of antibiotics in feed for animals such as cattle and sheep, it helps to produce high-quality, low cost food. Antibiotics help to keep animals disease free. They also help animals to grow. Animals get fatter quicker because they do not waste energy trying to overcome illness.

The use of antibiotics in livestock feed means that there is a higher risk of antibiotic-resistant bacteria developing. The rapid reproduction of bacteria means there is always a chance that a population of bacteria will develop which is antibiotic-resistant. These could be dangerous to human health.

a) Explain how a population of antibiotic-resistant bacteria might develop from non-resistant bacteria.

....

....

....

....

....

(3 marks)

b) Do you think that farmers should be allowed to put low doses of antibiotics in animal feed?

Explain the reasons for your answer.

....

....

....

(2 marks)

5

3 The table opposite shows changes in resistance to the antibiotic penicillin in one species of bacterium between 1991 and 1996.

A doctor was asked to treat a patient who had a sore throat.

a) How does penicillin help to treat infection?

....

(1 mark)

Years	Percentage of cases where bacteria were resistant to penicillin
1991–92	7
1993–94	14
1995–96	22

b) Use the data in the table to suggest why the doctor should not prescribe penicillin.

Marks

....

....

(2 marks)

3

4   a) The MMR vaccine is designed to protect us from three diseases caused by viruses. The vaccine is made of virus particles which have been modified to stop them producing the full effects of the diseases.

The vaccine is given to children aged 12 to 15 months. A second dose is given when children reach 3 to 5 years.

   i   Name the three diseases that are prevented by the MMR vaccine.

....

(2 marks)

   ii Explain how vaccines like MMR work on the body's immune system to prevent any further infection by the viruses.

....

....

....

(4 marks)

   b) The MMR vaccine has been very successful in preventing disease but it can make young children ill. The table below is taken from a NHS leaflet that compares the risks of using the MMR vaccine with the risks of not using the MMR vaccine.

Condition	Children affected after the natural disease	Children affected after the first dose of MMR
Convulsions	1 in 200	1 in 1000
Meningitis or encephalitis	1 in 200 to 1 in 5000	Less than 1 in a million
Conditions affecting blood clotting	1 in 3000 to 1 in 6000	1 in 22300
Deaths	1 in 2500 to 1 in 5000	0

Use the data in the table to explain why parents are advised to get their child vaccinated with the MMR vaccine even though it could make their child ill.

....

....

....

(3 marks)

9

23 Using microorganisms

▶ **Think About:**

1 What are the four main types of microorganism?

2 What do scientists usually grow microorganisms on?

3 Apart from being useful what else can microrganisms do?

4 Which group of microorganisms include moulds?

5 What do we call the branch of science that makes commercial use of microorganisms?

▶ **Fungi**

Moulds and yeast are examples of fungi.

Yeasts are single celled with:
- a nucleus,
- cytoplasm,
- a cell membrane,
- a cell wall.

Moulds have thread-like **hyphae** with walls surrounding:
- many nuclei,
- cytoplasm.

They do not contain separate cells.

Yeast can respire either **aerobically** (with oxygen), or **anaerobically** (without oxygen).
Aerobic respiration produces energy, carbon dioxide and water.
Anaerobic respiration produces less energy, carbon dioxide and ethanol – this is **fermentation**.

Microorganisms have been used for thousands of years to make food and drink.

Baking
- yeast is mixed with flour and water,
- this mixture is kept warm,
- carbon dioxide from respiration makes the dough rise,
- baking the bread makes the gas bubbles expand, making the bread light.

Brewing beer
- enzymes break down starch in barley grains into a sugary solution,
- this is called malting,
- the sugary solution is fermented by yeast,
- finally hops are added for flavour.

Making yoghurt
- some bacteria is added to warm milk,
- the bacteria ferment the milk sugar producing lactic acid,
- this causes the milk to clot into solid yoghurt.

Cheese making
- bacteria added to warm milk (different bacteria this time),
- curds (more solid than yoghurt) are produced,
- curds are separated from the liquid whey,
- bacteria and moulds are added to the curds to ripen.

Answers:
1. bacteria, fungi, viruses, single celled organisms 2. agar
3. cause disease 4. fungi 5. Biotechnology

▶ Using microorganisms on a large scale

> **Microorganisms can be grown in large fermenters to produce large quantities of useful products e.g. antibiotics.**

Industrial fermenters like this usually have:

- an air supply to provide oxygen for respiration;
- a stirrer to maintain an even temperature and keep the microorganisms in suspension;
- a water cooled jacket to remove heat made by respiration;
- pH, oxygen and temperature monitors.

If the mould *Penicillium* is grown in a fermenter with a suitable medium it will make the antibiotic penicillin – *but only when most of the nutrients have been used up*.

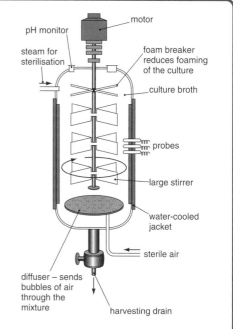

This type of industrial fermenter allows for continuous cultivation

H

▶ Fuels from microorganisms

A lot of waste material from living organisms contains carbohydrates. Microorganisms are involved in breaking down this material to produce a useful fuel known as **biogas**. Biogas is mainly **methane** and it is made by **anaerobic fermentation**.

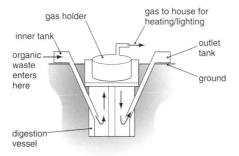

Ethanol-based fuels can also be made by anaerobic fermentation of sugar cane juices and glucose from maize starch. In some countries this is a good alternative to fossil-based fuels like petrol.

▶ Using microorganisms safely

Microorganisms are often grown on a **culture medium** in Petri dishes. This medium contains carbohydrates for energy plus mineral ions and sometimes protein and vitamins.

To prepare uncontaminated cultures:

- all equipment must be **sterilised** to kill unwanted microorganisms;
- the **inoculating loops** used to transfer the microorganisms must be sterilised in a flame;
- the Petri dish lid must be secured with tape to prevent microbes entering from the air;
- in schools cultures must be kept at a maximum of 25°C to prevent the growth of microorganisms dangerous to humans (pathogens).

In industry higher temperatures can be used to produce faster growth.

More in *Biology for You*, pages 308–319.

Take care:

- Many questions mention 'Aseptic techniques' when working with microbes. 'Aseptic' means you exclude all the microbes you don't want.
- In the production of cheese, yoghurt, wine, beer, bread and soy sauce, you need to remember the ingredients, the conditions used and the microorganisms involved.
- Remember the differences between batch and continuous cultivation.

Examination Questions – Using microorganisms

1 Living cells are used to make beer and yoghurt.

Marks

  a) Complete each sentence by using the correct words from the list.

alcohol	fructose	lactic acid	milk sugar
oxygen	protein	starch	sugar

    In beer-making, yeast converts .... into carbon dioxide

    and ....

    In yoghurt-making, bacteria convert .... into ....

(4 marks)

4

2 Yeast can be used to make bread.

Use the information given in the recipe below to help you answer the questions that follow.

RECIPE FOR WHITE BREAD

This recipe makes 2 × 500 g loaves.

Ingredients: 750 g of strong white bread flour   1 sachet of dried yeast

                      10 g of salt   450 ml of warm water (40°C)

                             25 g of white vegetable fat

1. Mix the flour with the salt and rub in the fat. Add the yeast and mix all the ingredients together.
2. Make a well in the centre of the mixture and add the warm water. Mix and knead for 10 minutes to a soft elastic dough.
3. Shape the dough and place into the bread tin. Cover with a clean tea towel and leave in a warm place for 45 minutes.
4. Bake at 230°C for 40 minutes.
5. Remove the loaf from the oven and allow to cool on a rack.

---

  a) When the dough is left in a warm place for 45 minutes it doubles in size.
     The yeast grows and uses glucose from the flour to produce energy.

Glucose → alcohol + carbon dioxide

    i Give the name for this energy-producing process.

    ....

(1 mark)

    ii Why does the dough double in size?

    ....

    ....

(1 mark)

    iii The process produces alcohol.
       Explain why there is no alcohol in a loaf of bread.

    ....

    ....

(2 marks)

b) A student carried out an experiment to investigate the growth of yeast.

Method

1. Label three glass bottles **A**, **B**, **C**.

2. Make up the bottles as follows:

3. Shake each bottle and seal with a deflated balloon.

4. Stand the bottles in a bowl of warm water (40°C) for 45 minutes.

Bottle	Contents
A	15 ml of water
B	2.5 g of yeast and 15 ml of water
C	5 g of glucose, 2.5 g of yeast and 15 ml of water

5. Watch what happens to the contents of the bottles and to the balloons.

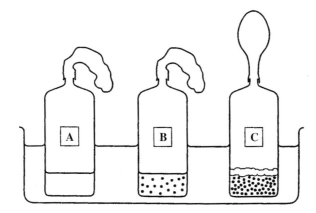

The student recorded the results in a table.

Balloon starts to inflate

The student carried out two further experiments using the mixtures from the bottles.

Bottle	Contents
A	No change
B	Yeast forms a suspension in water
C	Frothy suspension in bottle Balloon starts to inflate

1. He examined a drop of the mixture from each bottle under a simple light microscope.

2. He re-measured the mass of the yeast in Bottle **C**.

i Compare what the student might see in one drop of the mixture from bottle B with what he might see in one drop from bottle C.

....

....

....

(2 marks)

ii Describe an experiment to measure the mass of yeast in bottle C at the end of the experiment.

....

....

....

(3 marks)

9

Examination answers and tips

TOPIC 1 – Cells

Year 10 questions

1 1 cell membrane
   2 passes information to other cells
   3 controls the activities of the cell
   4 cytoplasm

2 1 absorbs light energy to make food
   2 strengthens the cell
   3 controls the activities of the cell
   4 contains cell sap

3 1 nucleus
   2 cell membrane
   3 cell wall
   4 cytoplasm

4 they are found in the cytoplasm
   they release energy during respiration

Year 11 questions

1 a) A cytoplasm   B cell membrane   C nucleus

   b) 0.045 mm

   c) C

   d) The sperm has a flexible tail.   6

2 a) i Nucleus
         Controls the activities of the cell.

      ii Cytoplasm
         Where most of the chemical reactions take place

      iii Cell membrane
         This structure controls the passage of
         substances in and out of the cell.

   b) i Plant cells have a wall which strengthens the cell.
      ii Plant cells often have chloroplasts which
         absorb light energy to make food.
      iii Plant cells often have a permanent vacuole
         filled with cell sap.   9

Examiner's Tip ✓

*Remember that the cells in the roots of plants do
not have chloroplasts. Also, some plant cells lack
a permanent, sap-filled vacuole. So it is better,
more accurate, to include 'often' in your answer
to b)i and ii above.*

TOPIC 2 – Digestion

Year 10 questions

1 1 stomach
   2 pancreas
   3 large intestine
   4 small intestine   4

2 lipase and protease   1

3 B   1

4 D   1

5 D   1

6 C   1

Year 11 questions

1 a) small intestine
        blood
        anus

   b) i <u>intestines</u>
       ii 12–24 hours   6

Examiner's Tip ✓

*Include units in your answers. There are usually
marks awarded for them.*

2 a) starch
        sugar
        protein
        amino acids

   b) Because they are insoluble.
       Digestion breaks them down into soluble products.
       The soluble products can be absorbed through
       the wall of the intestine   6

Examiner's Tip ✓

*Even when a question is worth two marks only,
there are often more than two things that may be
credited.*

Examination answers and tips

TOPIC 3 – Breathing and respiration
Year 10 questions

1 D

2 D

3 D

4 A

5 A

6 1 oxygen

2 glucose

3 lactic acid

4 water

7 A

Year 11 questions

1 a) i thorax

ii A trachea

B (left) bronchus

C rib

D heart

E diaphragm

b) Breathing is necessary because all living cells in the body respire. The breathing system moves air into and out of the body. This means that oxygen from the air can diffuse into the blood stream to be used in respiration. Respiration produces a potentially poisonous waste gas carbon dioxide. Carbon dioxide diffuses out of the blood into the air in the lungs. Breathing gets rid of this gas.   9

Examiner's Tip ✓

There are many points that you might want to use here. Each of the sentences contains a valid point that could be worth a mark on the mark scheme. Try to sort out a sensible order before you start writing things down.

2 a) 6 units of lactic acid are present at the end of the 5 minutes of exercise. Blood lactic acid concentration continues to rise for a further 5 minutes after exercise has ceased. A maximum concentration of 10 units is achieved 10 minutes after the exercise began. Blood lactic acid concentration falls steeply during the next 10 minutes and at a slower rate for the next 40 minutes. The resting level of blood lactic acid had not been restored by the end of the 60 minute period.

b) i Because the muscle cells do not have enough oxygen. Lactic acid is produced by the incomplete oxidation of glucose.

Examiner's Tip ✓

This question asks for a reason not an explanation. Had the question asked you to 'Explain why the body …' then your answer might have included the following kind of statements. 'This occurs when the breathing and circulatory systems fail to deliver sufficient oxygen to the actively respiring muscle cells. The muscle cells then have to respire anaerobically producing lactic acid as a waste.' Look for the key-words and take guidance from the space available for your answer.

ii During vigorous exercise, muscles have to obtain some or most of their energy by anaerobic respiration. This releases lactic acid. Oxygen is needed to break down this waste to carbon dioxide and water. The oxygen that is needed is called an oxygen debt.   6

TOPIC 4 – Blood and circulation
Year 10 questions

1 2 plasma

3 platelets

1 red blood cell

4 white blood cell

2 C

3 C

4 C

Examination answers and tips

Year 11 questions

1 a) i U

ii W

iii Y

iv R

b) Oxygen enters the blood in the lungs and diffuses into the red blood cells. Oxygen combines with the pigment haemoglobin present in the red blood cell. Oxyhaemoglobin is formed. When a red blood cell arrives in a tissue where oxygen concentration is low, oxyhaemoglobin breaks down, oxygen is released and haemoglobin is reformed.
The oxygen is then available for use by the cells of the tissue.   7

2 a) Y. Veins have relatively thin walls. The wall of Y is thinner, representing little muscle and elastic tissue. Y also has a large lumen. This is a characteristic of a vein.

b) muscle tissue   elastic tissue

c) Valves prevent backflow.   4

TOPIC 5 – Disease

Year 10 questions

1 A and C

2 A and B

3 A

4 3 flu virus

1 salmonella

2 typhoid

Year 11 questions

1 a) A   protein coat

B   genes

C   cell wall

D   cytoplasm

b) 1 and 2   Two of the following:
Skin acts as a barrier.
Mucus in air passages traps air-borne pathogens.

Blood clot seals wound.   6

2 a) 1 and 2   Two of the following:
bacterium
virus
fungus
protist

b) Mucus is sticky, trapping airborne pathogens and particles likely to do damage.

c) Stomach

d) White blood cells   6

TOPIC 6 – Diffusion

Year 10 questions

1 B

2 B

3 A

4 D

5 1 B

2 C

3 D

4 A

6 1 long

2 folded

3 increased

4 villi

5 capillaries

Year 11 questions

1 Oxygen dissolves in the moisture in the alveoli. Oxygen concentration is lower in the blood capillary close to the alveolus than in the alveolus itself.
The diffusion gradient present means that oxygen will diffuse across the alveolar and capillary membranes into the blood.
The opposite will be the case for carbon dioxide.   4

2 a) Diffusion is the random movement of particles of a gas or a substance in solution. The movement is generated by the kinetic energy associated with the particles.

b) The net direction of diffusion is from a region of higher concentration to one of lower concentration. This would lead to equilibrium, with the particles evenly distributed throughout the area to which they are admitted.

c) The size of the difference in concentration of a particle will be one factor that determines its rate of diffusion. The difference is described as a concentration gradient. The steeper the gradient is, the faster the rate of diffusion will be. Temperature will also affect the rate at which a particle will diffuse. Increasing the temperature will increase the rate of diffusion. **7**

TOPIC 7 – Photosynthesis
Year 10 questions

1 C

2 D

3 D

4 B

5 1 carries sugar away from the leaf
   2 controls water loss from the leaf
   3 where most glucose is produced
   4 a waxy material

Year 11 questions

1 a) i water   oxygen
     ii chlorophyll
  b) i Carbon dioxide is a substrate for the process. If there is none available photosynthesis cannot take place, even in bright sunlight. If there is a low concentration of carbon dioxide available, photosynthesis can take place but slowly, stopping when the carbon dioxide has been used up. If there is a higher concentration, photosynthesis will proceed more quickly. The amount of carbon dioxide will limit the rate of the process. If there is an excess of carbon dioxide the rate of the process is no longer limited by carbon dioxide.
     ii temperature **6**

2 a) The process does not start until the temperature reaches 3°C.
Rate increases between 3°C and 14°C.
Between 14°C and 35°C the rate stays the same.
Above 35°C the rate of the process decreases.

Examiner's Tip ✓
Remember to refer to specific data in questions involving graphs and/or tables.

  b) i photosynthesis
     ii oxygen

  c) 1,2 and 3. Three of the following:
Maize starts to produce glucose at a higher temperature.
Temperature limits the rate of glucose production over a greater range of temperature in maize (6°C to 30°C).
Rate levels out at 30°C in maize.
Rate does not decrease at 40°C (the highest temperature recorded). **9**

TOPIC 8 – Transport in plants
Year 10 questions

1 D

2 D

3 A

4 C

Year 11 questions

1 a) i Water is absorbed by the plant through root hair cells.
Large surface area increases the rate of absorption.

     ii Some substances can pass through the surface others cannot.

     iii Three of the following points:
Root hair cell membranes are partially permeable.
A concentration gradient for water is present across the membranes.
There is a higher concentration of water outside the cell compared to the cell sap in the vacuoles.
Therefore water moves into the cell by osmosis.

Examination answers and tips

b) i Two of the following points:
The uptake of mineral salts by root hair cells
The uptake of glucose by cells of the small intestine
The reabsorption of glucose from the kidney tubules back into the blood

ii to provide energy from respiration   **10**

TOPIC 9.1 – Plant hormones

1 shoot Y has grown more than shoot X
shoot Y has grown towards light from one side but shoot X has not

2 roots grow in the direction of the force of gravity
shoots grow towards light

3 1 inhibits
2 light
3 auxin
4 stimulate
5 gravity

TOPIC 9.2 – Drugs
Year 10 question

1 1 tobacco
2 alcohol
3 nicotine
4 carbon monoxide

Year 11 questions

1 Inhaled solvents will damage the cells in the airways and in the lungs.
Inhaled solvents are absorbed into the blood stream in the lungs.
Blood cells and blood vessels are likely to be damaged as are the tissues and organs visited by the blood.
Brain cells will be affected and consequently the behaviour of the individual will be abnormal.
The liver is involved in the breakdown of a variety of compounds as a normal function. Consequently, inhalation of solvents may lead to liver damage.   **3**

2 a) Depressants slow down the nervous system.

b) Amphetamines and cocaine would speed up the nervous system.

c) i A person develops a tolerance to a drug if he/she has to take increasing amounts of the drug to get the same effect.

ii Addiction means that a person has become so dependent on a drug that they have to take it regularly

iii Withdrawal symptoms can occur if an addicted person stops taking a particular drug.   **5**

TOPIC 10 – Nervous system
Year 10 questions

1 1 neurones
2 impulses
3 reflex
4 protect

2 D

3 A

4 C

5 B

6 B

7 D

Year 11 questions

1 a) i cornea
ii To refract or bend the light to focus it onto the retina

b) i iris
ii To open up or close down the pupil.
It makes the pupil dilate or constrict.
It does this using two sets of antagonistic muscles. Contraction of radial muscles dilates the pupil and contraction of circular muscles constricts it.   **8**

Examiner's Tip ✓
Muscles often work in antagonistic pairs. The contraction of one muscle reverses the effect of the contraction of the other.

2 a) Two of: touch, pressure, pain and temperature change

 b) i It acts as a junction between two consecutive neurones. It enables communication between the two nerve cells.

  ii Impulses arriving at a synapse stimulate the release of a chemical into the synapse. The chemical crosses the synapse. This initiates the generation of impulses in the next neurone.

 c) Flow diagram should include:

  stimulus → receptor → sensory neurone → relay neurone → motor neurone → effector → response

  10

Examiner's Tip ✓

The relay neurone will be in an area referred to as a coordinator. This will be the spinal cord for a spinal reflex e.g. limb withdrawal reflex and the brain for a cranial reflex e.g. blinking.

TOPIC 11 – Homeostasis
Year 10 questions

1 1 lungs
  2 kidneys
  3 pancreas
  4 bladder

2 C

3 C

4 C

5 B

6 skin and thermoregulatory centre

7 A

8 B

Year 11 question

1 a) i 6
  ii 5

 b) i pancreas
  ii Between 1 and 2 hours

 c) High concentration of glucose in the plasma will reduce the water potential of the blood. Normally the body attempts to maintain an osmotic balance. An exaggerated water potential gradient will arise between the tissues and the blood plasma. Consequently, cells bathed by the tissue fluid will lose water. This can be harmful to the cells. **8**

TOPIC 12 – Excretion
Year 10 questions

1 B

2 D

3 A

4 D

5 C

6 D

7 D

8 A

9 dissolved ions   sugars

10 C

Year 11 questions

1 a) 3 segments for 'breath'
   10 segments for 'sweat'
   6 segments for 'urine'

 b) carbon dioxide
   by **respiration**
   in **breath**
   urea
   from **amino acids**
   in **urine**   **7**

Examination answers and tips ✓

TOPIC 13 – Adaption and completion

1 1 The fur would act as an efficient insulator helping the fox to survive the cold conditions.

   2 The white colour would be advantageous providing the fox with good camouflage. It would be a more successful predator.   **3**

2 a) i Adapted to capture their prey in the dark. They have poorly developed vision.

     ii The bats have very large external ears to focus the sound waves into their ear canals.

     iii The bats are prey for owls, so the owls are their predators.

  b) There are not enough insects to support them. Winter temperatures might be too low. The bats might not be able to maintain their body temperature.

  c) 1 Warmer than average summers might have meant larger than average insect populations. More food meant more infant bats survived.

    2 More bats survived the winter hibernation.

    3 Fewer bats available as food in Years 1 and 2 could have limited the expansion of the owl population. Therefore there were fewer predators around and more bats survived to breed.   **7**

TOPIC 14 – Energy and biomass

1 a) 1 Organism X feeds on plant W.

    2 Organism X is eaten by the heron, bird Y.

  b) i Your answer should have been 'Z is a predator.' You could also have used Y as your chosen organism.

    ii W is a producer.   **4**

2 a) i The lynx population gets bigger.

    ii It decreased because the lynx feeds on hare and grouse. Both their populations were decreasing so there was less food to support the lynx population.

  b) The hare and grouse populations would increase because their predators had been removed. The vegetation population would come under pressure and decrease.

Competition between the hare and grouse populations for the plants for food would increase. One or probably both of the prey populations would decrease.

Examiner's Tip ✓
There are only two marks for this question so you would not be expected to write all of this for your marks. Each relevant point would probably be rewarded. If there are two marks on offer, then try to give two relevant statements.

c)

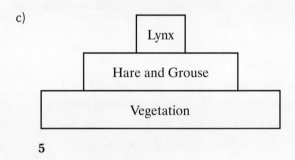

  5

3 a) This is called a food web.

  b) Phytoplankton are plants. They photosynthesise by trapping light energy. This process provides all the energy for all the dependent consumers.

  c) Cod and herring are sand eel predators. Therefore removing the predators could lead to an increase in the sand eel population. Seal and or minke whale populations might increase because they would have less competition for the sand eels therefore the sand eels might be predated by them instead.

  d) *Your answer could include two of the following.* There could be an adverse change in climate. The population could be limited by disease. A new consumer or predator could enter the community.   **11**

TOPIC 15 – Nutrient cycling

1 Plants use carbon dioxide from the air to make food. This process is called photosynthesis. Animals eat the plants as part of their food. Animals respire some of this food producing carbon dioxide as a waste gas which is released into the air.   **4**

Examination answers and tips

2 a) Either 'Bacteria' or 'Fungi'.

  b) i Decay is brought about by decomposers respiring the waste.
        More oxygen will accelerate this process

      ii Another factor could be temperature.　　**4**

3 decay　　warm　　moist　　grow　　**4**

4 a) i 47

      ii $165 \times \frac{47}{100}$
          77.55

      iii 49

  b) i A producer is an organism that produces complex organic molecules from simple inorganic ones.

      ii A consumer is an organism that feeds on producers or other consumers.

  c) The gas removed by photosynthesis is carbon dioxide

  d) Warmth and moisture.　　**9**

TOPIC 16 – Humans and the environment

1 a) Carbon dioxide will have been released into the atmosphere by machinery used in the cultivation process.
       Deforestation means that there are less mature forests to take in carbon dioxide for photosynthesis.
       Land clearance often involves burning of woodland. This will have released carbon dioxide.

  b) Polar ice caps could melt leading to raised sea-levels and the flooding of some low lying areas.
       More land becoming desert.

  c) The gas is methane.　　**5**

2 a) There will be a very high concentration of organic material and a very large population of bacteria at this point.
       The bacteria demand oxygen for respiration. Therefore the oxygen content of the water falls dramatically.

  b) Bacteria carry out decomposition.
       They decompose sewage and dead bacteria.
       Nitrifying bactgeria change ammonium salts in the sewage into nitrates.
       The process releases large quantities of nitrate.

  c) Populations of photosynthetic organisms will increase leading to an increase in oxygen released into the water.　　**7**

3 B Fossil fuels are burned.
   D Sulphur dioxide and nitrogen oxides are released.
   A Gases dissolve in rain.
   C Lakes and rivers become acidic so plants and animals die.　　**4**

TOPIC 17 – Genes and cell division

1 a) i The two glands are pituitary and ovaries.

      ii The two effects are to stimulate the ovaries and to alter the state of the uterine lining.

  b) One advantage is the process enables the woman to have a child by producing her own eggs.
       Disadvantages include the relatively low success rate, the possibility of multiple births and the process is very expensive.　　**7**

2 a) The gametes are B and F.

  b) The cells which have chromosomes in pairs are A, C, E, D.

  c) The cells which divide by meiosis are A and E.

  d) C and D have identical genetic information.　　**4**

3 a) They have replicated or 'doubled-up' by dividing along their length.

  b) The chromosome arrangement shown in cell 'headed' stage 1 should be shown in each of the cells.

  c) The alleles will be 'Aa'.　　**4**

TOPIC 18 – Artificial selection and genetic engineering

1 Arguments *for* might include:
  greater profitability;
  healthier product.

  Arguments *against* might include:
  ethical issues;
  genes might spread to other species by pollination;
  change may affect other organisms in the food chain;
  may adversely change the plants resistance to disease.　　**4**

Examiner's Tip ✓
You will need to refer to both 'for' and 'against' to qualify for full marks.

Examination answers and tips

2 a) A gene is a short section of DNA.

DNA is composed of bases arranged in a specific order.

Bases provide the code for specific amino acids. A specific sequence of amino acids produces a specific protein e.g. the one that is the glue.

b) The gene coding for the production of glue is isolated. Enzymes are used to cut open the DNA in the plant cells. Other enzymes attach the gene coding for the glue production into the plant DNA. Asexual reproduction (cloning) of the plants results in many plants capable of producing the glue. **7**

3 a) The process where individuals (animals or plants) are chosen because they have the characteristics we want.
These individuals are used to breed from.

b) Farmers wanted to produce a horse that was large and strong.
They would have selected a stallion and mare which had those features to produce the individual shown in the photograph. **4**

TOPIC 19 – Evolution

1 a) If conditions for decay are absent the animal may be preserved.
Hard parts (such as bone) are buried in sediment and turned to rock.
Soft parts can be replaced with hard minerals.

b) It is possible to use fossils to look for similarities and differences shown by organisms from the past with those alive today.
Fossils help us to work out evolutionary pathways.

c) Perhaps changes in the environment led to more firm ground being present in the animal's habitat.
Originally the horse-like mammal had feet more suitable for running on marshy ground.
Some of their offspring may have had fewer bones in their feet. These would have had an advantage in escaping from predators on the firmer ground.
They would have survived to breed passing on their advantageous genes.
Each successive generation may have experienced this selective process leading to feet such as those shown in the modern horse. **9**

2 Lamarckism argues that change occurs as a result of changes acquired during a lifetime.
Darwinism argues that the 'long-leggedness' referred to in the question arises because of the possession of particular genetic material.
Lamarckism suggests that continual stretching of the legs would have produced a change in the parents that could be passed on to their offspring.
Darwinism argues that some of the waders had longer legs than others because of their genetic make-up and these advantageous genes could be passed on to their offspring. **4**

TOPIC 20 – Genetics

1 DNA   23   XX   XY   recessive   dominant   **6**

2 a) genes   sperm

b) The embryo from which the son developed was formed from a fertilised egg. Some of his characteristics would have been determined by the genes in the egg which came from his mother. **3**

3 a) DNA is a very long molecule.
It is made up of two strands.
Each strand is formed from a large number of bases.
There are four different types of base.

b) In any particular type of DNA the bases are arranged in a specific order.
Three bases, one after the other, form a code for a specific amino acid.
Base order over a length of DNA therefore provides a code for a specific amino acid order.
The order in which amino acids are linked together is important. It is this order that determines which protein is assembled.
In this way, DNA determines the order in which amino acids are assembled to form specific proteins.

c) Some individuals are affected by genetic disease. If genetic engineering can be employed to overcome this it would be beneficial.
Organs or tissues could be grown in animals for transplant into individuals who need them.
There are however ethical issues that need to be considered. These will obviously depend on an individual's views. Some for example would object strongly in that it is wrong to interfere with natural processes to this degree. **7**

4 a) These people are called carriers.

b)

	Nn		Parent
	N	n	Gametes
N	NN	Nn	Offspring
n	Nn	nn	

Nn

Has cystic fibrosis

c) i These changes are called mutations.

   ii 1 Exposure to ionising radiations such as UV or X-ray or radiation from a radioactive source.

   2 Certain chemicals called mutagens will cause changes in genes. **7**

TOPIC 21 – Movement and feeding

1 a) The fish has a streamlined shape. This reduces the resistance when the fish moves through the water.

b) 1 Tail fin labelled A.
   2 One of the paired fins labelled B.

Examiner's Tip ✓

Use a rule to label diagrams. Make sure the line starts precisely on the structure or feature involved. Do not leave the end of the line floating around in space unless that's what you want to label.

c) The fish has an air-filled swim bladder that gives it buoyancy. **5**

2

Tissue	Properties	Function
bone	Hard	**Resists compression. bending and stretching**
ligament	**Tensile strength and some elasticity**	Keeps the joint together but allows it to bend without easily dislocating
cartilage	**Strong but flexible**	**Allows compression and absorbs shock**
tendon	Has tensile strength and little elasticity	**Transfers force from muscle to bone without stretching**

5

Examiner's Tip ✓

Remember: think things through carefully before you start to fill in the table there is only a limited amount of space. It is difficult if you have to make corrections after you have started.

3 a) Mosquito mouth parts are adapted to suck blood from capillaries.

The insect has a proboscis with which it penetrates the skin. This structure is a sharp hollow tube. Muscles in the throat of the insect draw blood from the capillary.

The insect releases saliva into the wound. The saliva contains an anti-coagulant to stop the blood clotting on its way out of the capillary.

b) The dentition of a dog shows incisors on the top jaw where the sheep has a horny pad.

There are canines present on the upper and lower jaw of the dog. These are absent in the sheep.

The dog does not have a diastema (space) which is a characteristic of the sheep.

The cutting edges of the premolars and molars of the sheep interlock. Those in the dog pass each other the upper molars outside the lower molars.

The cutting edges of the dog's molars are like blades whereas the molar teeth of the sheep are flattened as grinding surfaces.

The jaw hinge is lower on the dog skull.

There is a bigger surface area for muscle attachment above the hinge, behind the eye orbit on the dog's skull. This enlarged area is below the hinge and in front of the eye orbit in the sheep skull. **10**

Examiner's Tip ✓

Remember: This question asks you to describe differences therefore it is important that you make it clear what the difference is. You must make comparative statements or link two descriptive statements with link words such as 'whereas' or 'but in the case of the ….'
Do not leave it to the examiner to make the distinction.

Examination answers and tips ✓

TOPIC 22 – Controlling disease

1 antigens   white   antibodies
pathogen   active   **5**

2 a) Bacteria may divide once every 20 minutes under favourable conditions.

   Mutations may occur during cell division. Reproducing at the rate that bacteria do the chance of this occurring is high.

   A mutation may provide the bacterial cell with the ability to resist an antibiotic.

   b) When low doses of antibiotic are given to farm animals the sensitive bacteria will die but the resistant ones will survive.

   The resistant forms then thrive because the competition is reduced and become the dominant form.   **5**

3 a) Penicillin kills the bacteria causing the infection.

   b) Some of the bacteria in a population that is sensitive to penicillin are not killed by the drug. These are the resistant forms.
   The data suggest that there has been a trebling of the number of cases where penicillin resistant pathogens were reported.
   7% to 22% over the five year period.
   Over prescription of penicillin may be responsible for the increase in frequency of resistance.   **3**

4 a) i   Mumps   Measles   Rubella
      ii The viruses are antigens.
          Two types of white blood cells are involved in the immune response.
          T cells have receptors that attach to the antigen and destroy them.
          B cells produce antibodies in response to the antigens.
          T cells and B cells are specific to a particular antigen.

There will be therefore T and B cells for each of the three viruses present in the MMR vaccine. Some of the B cells act as memory cells so that should the antigen appear in the blood stream at a later date then the body can respond very rapidly to destroy the pathogen.

   b) There is a risk involved in using the vaccine.
   The vaccine contains dead or modified pathogens and therefore may produce some of the problems associated with the natural diseases.
   The frequency of occurrence in children with the vaccine however is much smaller when compared to the natural disease.
   E.g. of supporting data include 1 in 200 children having convulsions after the natural disease and 1 in 1000 after the first MMR dose.   **9**

TOPIC 23 – Using microorganisms

1 sugar   alcohol   milk sugar   lactic acid   **4**

2 a) i   The energy-producing process is called anaerobic respiration but in this context it is usually called fermentation.

      ii The dough doubles in size because it is inflated by the carbon dioxide released.

      iii The bread is cooked. At the temperature necessary to cook the bread the alcohol evaporates.

   b) i   He would see yeast cells in the sample from B.
          The yeast cells in the sample from C would be dividing or budding and there would be a much larger number of them.

      ii Separate the yeast cells from the culture medium.
          Do this either by filtering or by centrifuging the sample.
          Find the mass of cells. Dry the sample to constant mass.   **9**

Index

Published in 2005 by:
Nelson Thornes Ltd
Delta Place
27 Bath Road
CHELTENHAM
GL53 7TH
United Kingdom

05 06 07 08 09 / 10 9 8 7 6 5 4 3 2 1

A catalogue record for this book is available from the British Library

ISBN 0 7487 9582 0

Page make-up by Tech-Set
Printed in Croatia by Zrinski

Acknowledgements

I would particularly like to record my thanks to Nick Paul for writing the
Environment and Triple Award sections of this book.

We would like to thank examiners Bob McDuell and David Baylis for their help with
the examination questions, answers and tips.

AQA acknowledgements

AQA examination questions are reproduced by permission of the Assessment and
Qualifications Alliance.

Chap. 1 Science: Biology (Modular) Module 1 Foundation March 2003 Q4; Science:
Biology (Modular) Module 2 Foundation March 2003 Q3; Science: Biology (Modular)
Module 1 Foundation June 2003 Q1; Science: Biology (Modular)
Module 1 Higher March 2003 Q14; Science: Double Award (Co-ordinated) Paper 1
Foundation November 2001 Q1; Chap. 2 Science: Biology (Modular) Module 1
Foundation March 2003 Q9; Science Double Award (Co-ordinated) June 2003 Q4;
Science: Single Award (Modular) Paper 1 Foundation June 2001 Q19;
Chap. 3 Science: Biology (Modular) Module 1 Foundation March 2003 Q8; Science:
Biology (Modular) Module 1 Foundation March 2003 Q2; Science: Biology (Modular)
Module 1 Higher March 2003 Q9.1; Science: Double Award (Co-ordinated) Paper 1
Higher Nov 2001 Q4; Science; Double Award Paper 1 Higher June 2003 Q17;
Chap. 4 Science: Biology (Modular) Module 1 Foundation March 2003 Q2; Science:
Biology (Modular) Module 1 Foundation March 2003 Q5; Science: Biology (Modular)
Module 1 Higher March 2003 Q10; Science: Double award (Co-ordinated) Paper 1
Foundation Nov 2001 Q8; ; Science: Double award (Co-ordinated) Paper 1 Higher
June 2001 Q3(b); Chap. 5 Science: Single Award (Co-ordinated) Paper 1 Foundation
June 2001 Q7; Science: Double Award (Co-ordinated) Paper 1 Foundation May
2002 Q5; Chap. 7 Science: Biology (Modular) Module 2 Foundation June 2003 Q9;
Science: Biology (Modular) Module 2 Foundation March 2003 Q5; Science: Double
Higher June 2001 Q17; Chap. 8 Science: Biology (Modular) Module 2 Foundation
June 2003 Q7; Science: Biology (Modular) Module 2 Foundation March 2003 Q10;
Science: Double Award (Co-ordinated) Paper 1 Foundation Nov 2001 Q10;
Chap. 9 Science: Biology (Modular) Module 2 Foundation June 2003 Q4;
Chap 12 Science: Double Award (Modular), Foundation 2003 Q8

Please note that the following AQA(NEAB) questions used on pages 11, 15, 19, 23,
27, 37, 41 are NOT from the live examinations for the current specification.

AQA take no responsibility for answers given to their questions within this publication.

Photograph acknowledgements

Alamy, p.82; Patrick Robert/Sygma/Corbis, p.86; Corel 21 (NT), p.82;
Gerry Ellis/Digital Vision JA (NT), p. 87; Photodisc 40 (NT), p.50.